Timely Tasks
for
Fast Finishers

7–9 Year Olds

Peter Clutterbuck

Brilliant Publications

We hope you and your pupils enjoy using this book. You might be interested in these other books published by Brilliant Publications:

Timely Tasks: 5–7 Year Olds	978-1-905780-00-6
Timely Tasks: 9–11 Year Olds	978-1-905780-02-0
Brilliant Activities for Gifted and Talented Children	978-1-903853-47-4
Thinking Strategies for the Successful Classroom: 5–7 Year Olds	978-1-905780-03-7
Thinking Strategies for the Successful Classroom: 7–9 Year Olds	978-1-905780-04-4
Thinking Strategies for the Successful Classroom: 9–11 Year Olds	978-1-905780-05-1

If you would like further information on these or other titles published by Brilliant Publications, please look at our website www.brilliantpublications.co.uk or write to the address below.

Published in the UK by Brilliant Publications

Sales:

BEBC (Brilliant Publications)
Albion Close, Parkstone, Poole, Dorset BH12 3LL
Tel: 0845 1309200 01202 712910
Fax: 0845 1309300
e-mail: brilliant@bebc.co.uk
website: www.brilliantpublications.co.uk

Editorial and Marketing:

10 Church View, Sparrow Hall Farm, Edlesborough, Dunstable,
Bedfordshire LU6 2ES
Tel: 01525 222292

The name Brilliant Publications and its logo are registered trademarks.

Written by Peter Clutterbuck
Typeset and designed by Bob Reyes
Illustrations by Greg Anderson-Clift
Cover by Lynda Murray
Text copyright © Peter Clutterbuck 2001
© 2001 Blake Publishing

This edition is for sale in the United Kingdom only. Originally published in Australia by Blake Publishing.

ISBN 978-1-905780-01-3

Printed 2007 in the UK
10 9 8 7 6 5 4 3 2 1

CONTENTS

Task Cards

Each word in the left box can be connected in some way with a word in the right box. Write the connecting word pairs on the lines.

horse	fish
scales	hump
down	glass
paper	heart
camel	duck
bottle	saddle
silk	worm
kidney	pen

_____   _____

_____   _____

_____   _____

_____   _____

_____   _____

_____   _____

_____   _____

_____   _____

Make a word

In five minutes see how many words you can write that contain 'oo'.

Now in five minutes see how many you can write that contain 'ee'.

Make a word

See how many words you can make by using the letters in the box. Each letter may be used only once in a word and no plurals are allowed.

m	t	a	e
c	p	l	s
k	i	b	n

Timely Tasks for Fast Finishers 7–9 Year Olds
© Blake Publishing

ENGLISH

Same letters

Two words in each line have exactly the same letters in them. Find them and circle them.

1. ant, ate, sea, tea, flea
2. flow, hold, wall, wolf, ball
3. want, pant, wisp, wasp, paws
4. lump, bump, limp, pest, plum
5. lame, lime, make, meal, sale
6. tame, bake, meat, lake, take

7. tail, mail, fail, lair, rail
8. read, feed, dare, care, bead
9. said, dine, edit, head, tide
10. bleat, label, table, stables, chest
11. care, pace, race, mace, fare
12. stare, star, mare, rats, hats

5 MINUTES

Cramped words

When this list of words was being typed it became very cramped. Can you work out what each word is? The clues below will help you. Write each word beside its clue.

mouseduckfoursickpinklionfirstcitydrysnakeshoespony

1. not well _____
2. large cat _____
3. reptile _____
4. number _____
5. small horse _____
6. opposite to last _____
7. large town _____

8. not wet _____
9. colour _____
10. farmyard bird _____
11. footwear _____
12. small creature that likes to eat cheese _____

10 MINUTES

ENGLISH

1. On the lines below, write the words which match the definitions.

2. Each word begins with one of the letters in the box. Cross out this letter in the box after you have used it.

3. Find a monkey and a vegetable in the leftover letters.

| *a* | *t* | *b* | *c* | *l* | *k* | *s* | *e* | *m* | *i* | *p* | *d* | *e* |

1. Animal with a hump
   _____

2. Baby cat
   _____

3. An insect that makes honey
   _____

4. Large animal with a trunk
   _____

5. We get it from cows
   _____

6. The number after 19
   _____

7. Animal that barks
   _____

8. Cup and...
   _____

9. It has rungs and you climb up it _____

10. Frozen water
    _____

5 MINUTES

Small words

Use the small words from the box to complete the names of these animals and birds.

| *bit* | *row* | *wall* | *key* | *can* |
| *rot* | *pen* | *edge* | *or* | *at* |

1. p l _ _ y p u s

2. h _ _ _ _ _ h o g

3. _ _ _ g u i n

4. m o n _ _ _ _

5. s p a r _ _ _ _

6. s _ _ _ _ _ o w

7. r a b _ _ _ _

8. s t _ _ k

9. p a r _ _ _ _

10. p e l i _ _ _ _

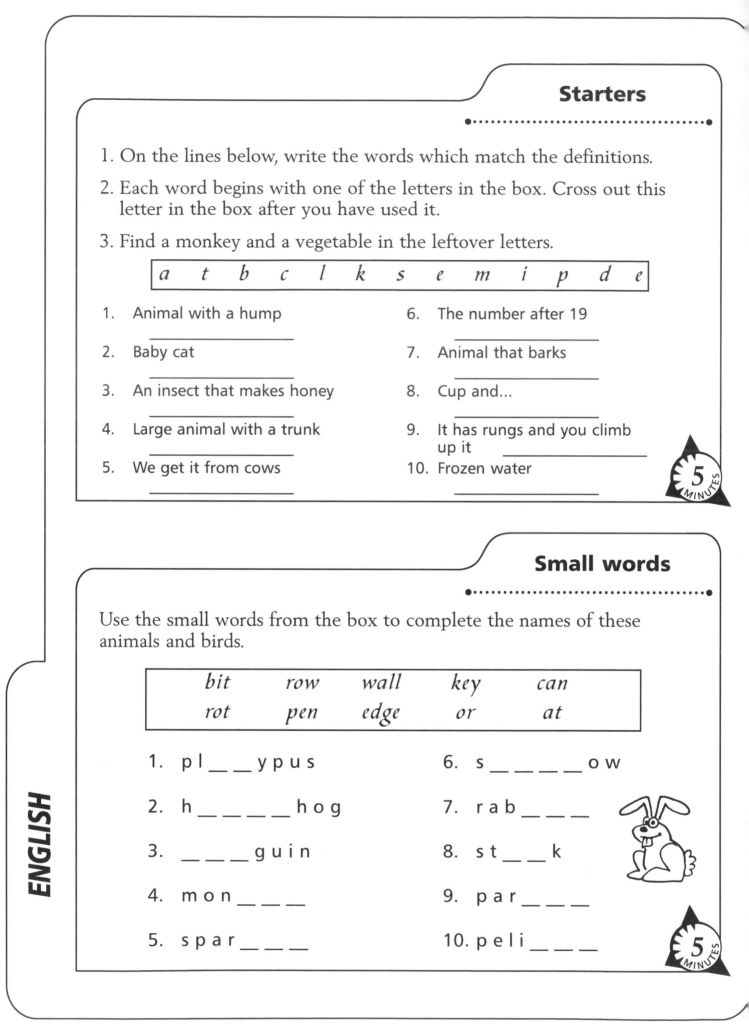

5 MINUTES

ENGLISH

Codes

a	b	c	d	e	f	g	h	i	j	k	l	m
✌	👌	👍	👎	☞	☛	☝	🖐	✋	☺	😐	☹	💣

n	o	p	q	r	s	t	u	v	w	x	y	z
☠	⚑	⚐	✈	☼	♦	❄	✝	☉	☿	✠	✡	☪

Can you decipher the codes to work out the names of the creatures below?

1. ☞⚑☼♦☞ _____
2. ☛⚑☠😐☞✡ _____
3. ☪☞👌☼✌ _____
4. 💣⚑✝♦☞ _____
5. ☝⚑✌❄ _____
6. ❄🖐👍☞☼ _____

7. ♦⚐✌☼☼⚑☿ _____
8. ☼⚑👌🖐☠ _____
9. ☞✌☹☞ _____
10. ♦☿✌☹⚑☿ _____
11. ⚐☞☠👍✝🖐☠ _____
12. ☞☹☞⚑⚐☝☠❄ _____

7 MINUTES

Picture this

Look at this picture of Brigit the Bricklayer. Write down the names of all the things in the picture that begin with B.

15 MINUTES

ENGLISH

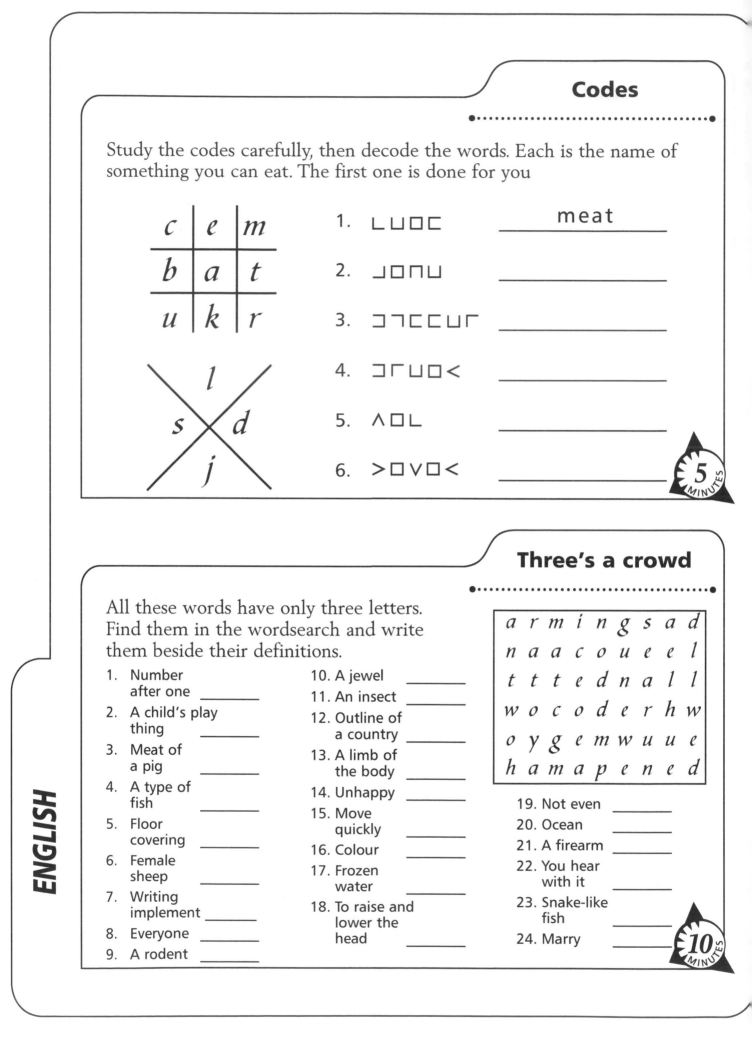

Codes

Study the codes carefully, then decode the words. Each is the name of something you can eat. The first one is done for you

c	e	m
b	a	t
u	k	r

s × d (with l above and j below)

1. � code   meat

2. ⎓⎓⎓⎓ _____

3. ⎓⎓⎓⎓⎓ _____

4. ⎓⎓⎓⎓⎓ _____

5. ⎓⎓⎓ _____

6. ⎓⎓⎓⎓⎓ _____

5 MINUTES

Three's a crowd

ENGLISH

All these words have only three letters. Find them in the wordsearch and write them beside their definitions.

1. Number after one _____
2. A child's play thing _____
3. Meat of a pig _____
4. A type of fish _____
5. Floor covering _____
6. Female sheep _____
7. Writing implement _____
8. Everyone _____
9. A rodent _____
10. A jewel _____
11. An insect _____
12. Outline of a country _____
13. A limb of the body _____
14. Unhappy _____
15. Move quickly _____
16. Colour _____
17. Frozen water _____
18. To raise and lower the head _____

a	r	m	i	n	g	s	a	d
n	a	a	c	o	u	e	e	l
t	t	t	e	d	n	a	l	l
w	o	c	o	d	e	r	h	w
o	y	g	e	m	w	u	u	e
h	a	m	a	p	e	n	e	d

19. Not even _____
20. Ocean _____
21. A firearm _____
22. You hear with it _____
23. Snake-like fish _____
24. Marry _____

10 MINUTES

Brilliant Publications

Timely Tasks for Fast Finishers 7–9 Year Olds
© Blake Publishing

Table words

In the table below, write words which begin with the letters in the top row.

The words must contain the number of letters indicated at the side of the table.

	m	o	a	n	s
2	me				
3		one			
4				nest	
5					
6					starve

10 MINUTES

Twin words

Find a word from the grid that matches a word in the list and write it beside its partner. The first one is done for you.

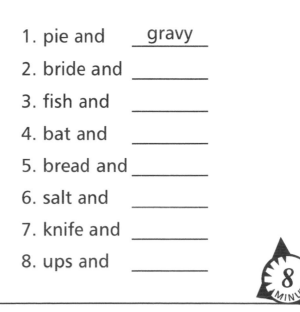

c	h	i	p	s	p
b	j	a	m	d	e
a	g	g	f	o	p
l	r	r	o	w	p
l	o	a	r	n	e
x	o	v	k	s	r
x	m	y	x	x	x

1. pie and ___gravy___
2. bride and _____
3. fish and _____
4. bat and _____
5. bread and _____
6. salt and _____
7. knife and _____
8. ups and _____

8 MINUTES

ENGLISH

Spell-well shape

Colour all the shapes *blue* that contain the *correct* spelling of a word.

Colour all the shapes **red** that have words **incorrectly** spelt.

If you do it correctly you will be able to discover the hidden shape.

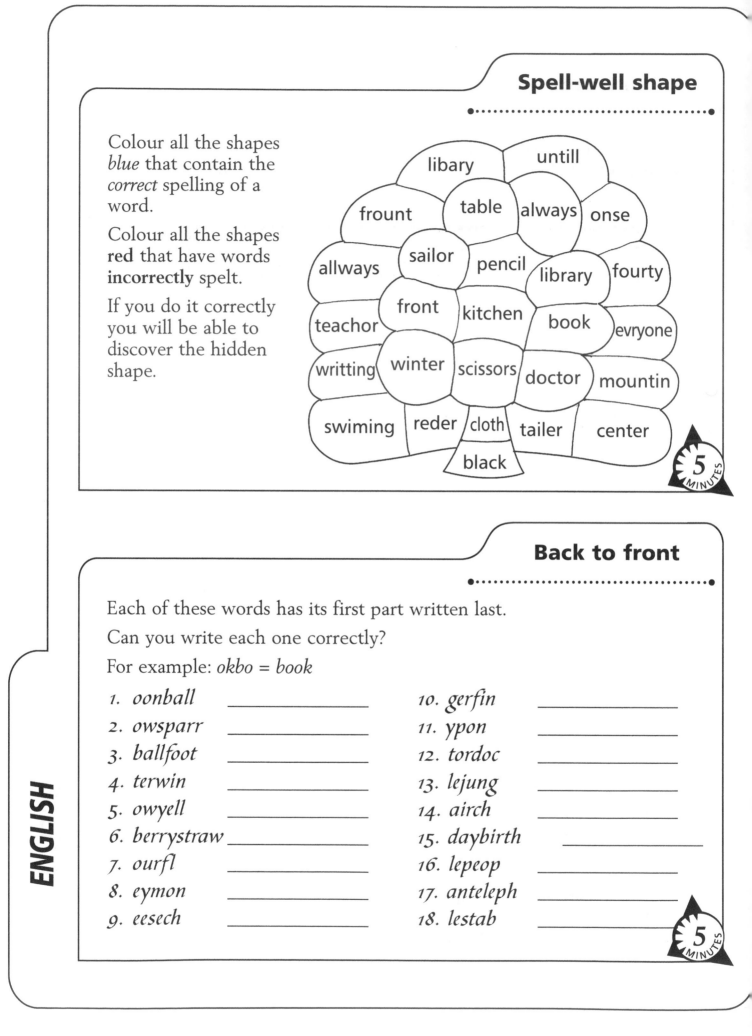

libary untill frount table always onse allways sailor pencil library fourty teachor front kitchen book evryone writting winter scissors doctor mountin swiming reder cloth tailer center black

5 MINUTES

Back to front

Each of these words has its first part written last.

Can you write each one correctly?

For example: *okbo = book*

1. *oonball* _____
2. *owsparr* _____
3. *ballfoot* _____
4. *terwin* _____
5. *owyell* _____
6. *berrystraw* _____
7. *ourfl* _____
8. *eymon* _____
9. *eesech* _____
10. *gerfin* _____
11. *ypon* _____
12. *tordoc* _____
13. *lejung* _____
14. *airch* _____
15. *daybirth* _____
16. *lepeop* _____
17. *anteleph* _____
18. *lestab* _____

5 MINUTES

ENGLISH

Magic squares

Unjumble the letters beside each clue. Write the answer across the squares. When you have finished you will find the same words also run downwards!

water container   (tnka)

boy's name   (lAna)

what people call you   (mnae)

leg joint   (nkee)

to whisk or agitate   (tsir)

movements of the ocean (dtie)

thought, notion   (eida)

harvest, mow   (prae)

8 MINUTES

Classifying

Place the words in the box in their correct tree below.

crimson	*lettuce*	*lizard*	*yellow*
cabbage	*penguin*	*violet*	*marrow*
ostrich	*crocodile*	*turnip*	*swallow*
gecko	*purple*	*sparrow*	*snake*

Colours   Vegetables   Birds   Reptiles

5 MINUTES

ENGLISH

Brilliant Publications

This page may be reproduced by the original purchaser for non-commercial classroom use.

Timely Tasks for Fast Finishers 7–9 Year Olds

© Blake Publishing

11

In each group of words, circle the one that is out of place. Give your reasons.

Your reasons

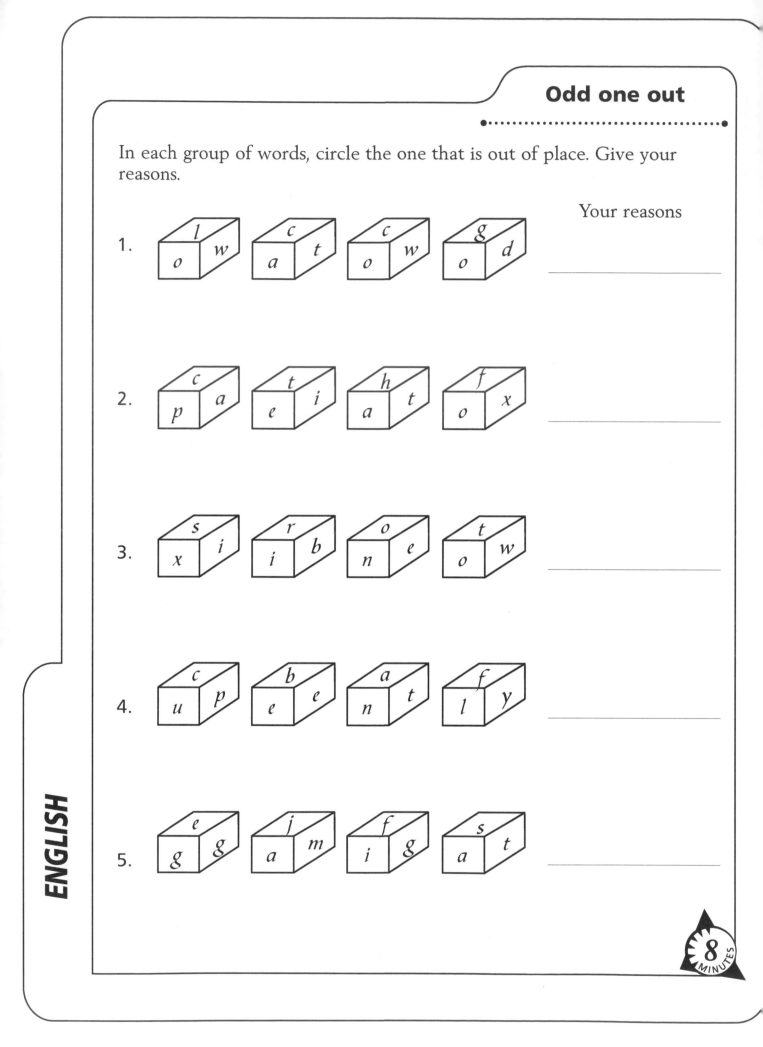

1. low cat cow god _____

2. cap tie hat fox _____

3. six rib one two _____

4. cup bee ant fly _____

5. egg jam fig sat _____

ENGLISH

12

Brilliant Publications
This page may be reproduced by the original purchaser for non-commercial classroom use.

Timely Tasks for Fast Finishers 7–9 Year Olds
© Blake Publishing

8 MINUTES

Hidden word

If you write down the first letter of these jumbled words and then add every second letter, you will find the name of something to eat.

1. *hxatmpbzusrtgxesr*

    _____

2. *pxetayczh*

    _____

3. *btaznxaxnpa*

    _____

4. *byuptztxeyr*

    _____

5. *cthpexexsye*

    _____

6. *mxatrxgxaprxitnxe*

    _____

7. *ltexmyopn*

    _____

8. *atpzrxixcyott*

    _____

3 MINUTES

Missing vowels

Add the missing vowels to complete each of these words.

1. __ n t __ l __ p __ (animal)

2. s c h __ __ l (place of learning)

3. t __ n n __ s (sport)

4. q __ __ s t __ __ n (opposite to answer)

5. t r __ c t __ r (farm machine)

6. __ c t __ g __ n (shape)

7. n __ w s p __ p __ r (something to be read)

8. m __ __ n t __ __ n (large hill)

9. m __ g p __ __ (bird)

10. l __ z __ r d (reptile)

11. l __ t t __ c __ (green leafy vegetable)

12. l __ b r __ r y (place for books)

5 MINUTES

ENGLISH

Brilliant Publications

This page may be reproduced by the original purchaser for non-commercial classroom use.

Timely Tasks for Fast Finishers 7–9 Year Olds

© Blake Publishing

13

'One' builder

Make ten words by adding a letter or group of letters to the word 'one'.

Add the letter or letters to the beginning, the end or both.

For example: someONE.

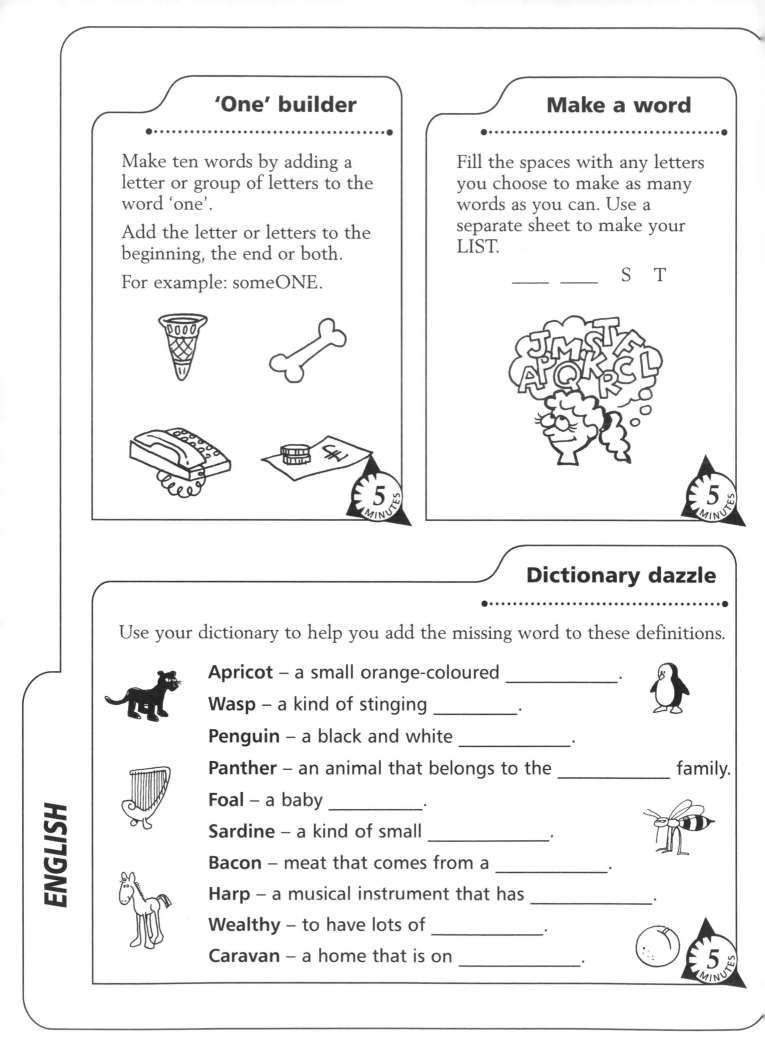

Make a word

Fill the spaces with any letters you choose to make as many words as you can. Use a separate sheet to make your LIST.

___ ___ S T

Dictionary dazzle

Use your dictionary to help you add the missing word to these definitions.

Apricot – a small orange-coloured _____.

Wasp – a kind of stinging _____.

Penguin – a black and white _____.

Panther – an animal that belongs to the _____ family.

Foal – a baby _____.

Sardine – a kind of small _____.

Bacon – meat that comes from a _____.

Harp – a musical instrument that has _____.

Wealthy – to have lots of _____.

Caravan – a home that is on _____.

Brilliant Publications

This page may be reproduced by the original purchaser for non-commercial classroom use.

Timely Tasks for Fast Finishers 7–9 Year Olds

© Blake Publishing

ENGLISH

Word road

How many words can you find in this word road? Start at 't'.

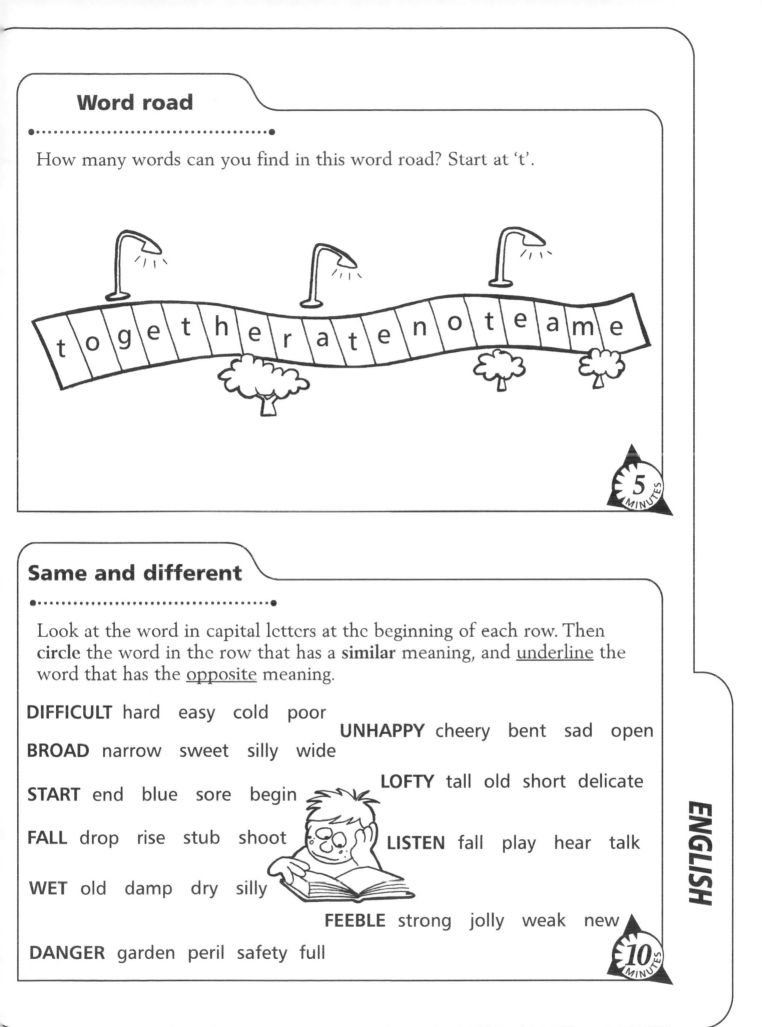

togetheratenoteame

5 MINUTES

Same and different

Look at the word in capital letters at the beginning of each row. Then **circle** the word in the row that has a **similar** meaning, and underline the word that has the opposite meaning.

DIFFICULT hard   easy   cold   poor

BROAD narrow   sweet   silly   wide

START end   blue   sore   begin

FALL drop   rise   stub   shoot

WET old   damp   dry   silly

DANGER garden   peril   safety   full

UNHAPPY cheery   bent   sad   open

LOFTY tall   old   short   delicate

LISTEN fall   play   hear   talk

FEEBLE strong   jolly   weak   new

10 MINUTES

ENGLISH

Brilliant Publications

This page may be reproduced by the original purchaser for non-commercial classroom use.

Timely Tasks for Fast Finishers 7–9 Year Olds

© Blake Publishing

15

Adding letters

Add one letter to each of the words below to make a word that fits the definition.

The letter may be added to any part of the word.

☆ **and** a body part _____

🎩 **cot** piece of clothing _____

☆ **fog** animal that hops _____

🎩 **net** a bird's home _____

☆ **pin** type of tree _____

🎩 **sip** a large boat _____

car a mark on the skin _____

bit used to catch fish _____

read food _____

stars steps _____

ban farm building _____

☆ 🎩 ☆ 🎩 ☆ 🎩 ☆ 🎩 ☆ 🎩 ☆ 🎩

5 MINUTES

Letter rows

1	k	p	l	o	n	m	q
2	t	p	s	o	x	t	v
3	e	t	v	e	e	w	b
4	m	o	n	k	e	y	s
5	a	i	u	o	e	a	u
6	i	f	e	d	b	c	a

1. Which row has only vowels? ____

2. In which rows do all the letters come after 'j' in the alphabet? ____

3. In which row does the same vowel appear three times? ____

4. Which row spells the name of some animals? ____

5. In which row do all the letters come before 'j' in the alphabet? ____

6. Make five words from the first four letters in row 2. ____

10 MINUTES

ENGLISH

Brilliant Publications

© Blake Publishing

Unscrambles

Unscramble and join the word parts in each line to make two words.
For example: bo fi ok sh = book, fish

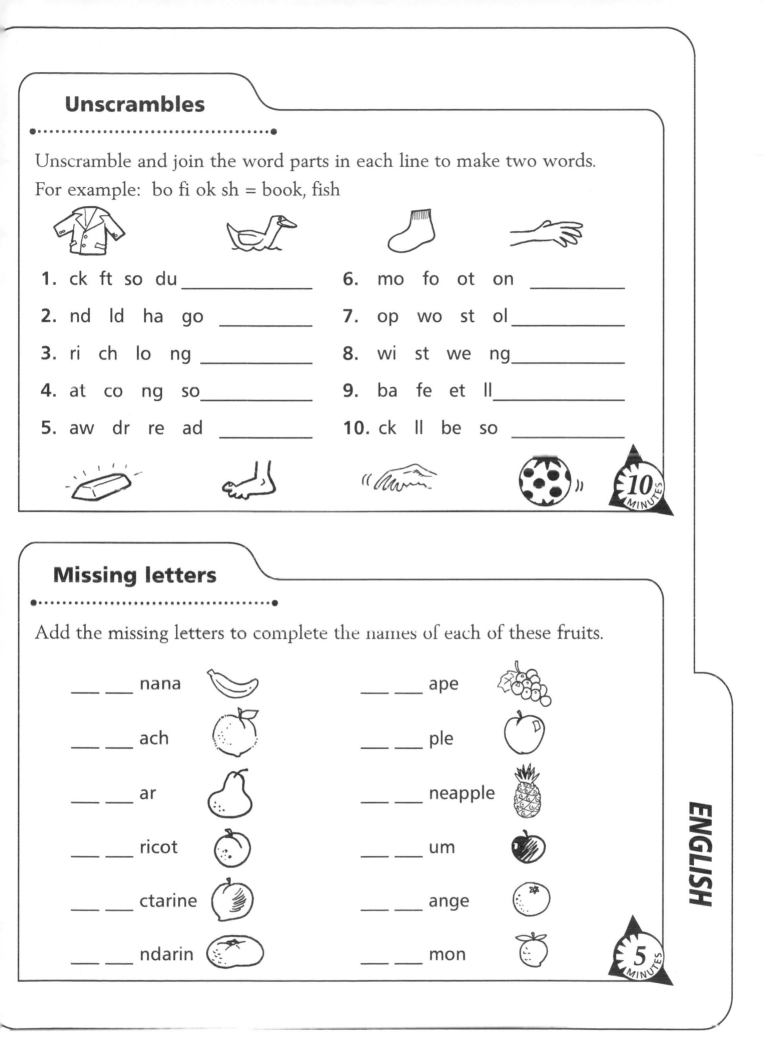

1. ck ft so du _____

2. nd ld ha go _____

3. ri ch lo ng _____

4. at co ng so _____

5. aw dr re ad _____

6. mo fo ot on _____

7. op wo st ol _____

8. wi st we ng _____

9. ba fe et ll _____

10. ck ll be so _____

10 MINUTES

Missing letters

Add the missing letters to complete the names of each of these fruits.

__ __ nana

__ __ ach

__ __ ar

__ __ ricot

__ __ ctarine

__ __ ndarin

__ __ ape

__ __ ple

__ __ neapple

__ __ um

__ __ ange

__ __ mon

5 MINUTES

ENGLISH

Brilliant Publications

This page may be reproduced by the original purchaser for non-commercial classroom use.

Timely Tasks for Fast Finishers 7–9 Year Olds

© Blake Publishing

17

Start with the first letter, write it down in column 1 then add every second letter and you will find a word to match part of the clue.

Now start at the second letter and do the same thing in column 2 and you'll find another word that belongs with the first word.

		Column 1	Column 2
1. f b l e y e	two insects	_____	_____
2. z t e i b g r e a r	two striped animals	_____	_____
3. c n h o i s n e	two parts of the face	_____	_____
4. t c a h b a l i e r	two pieces of furniture	_____	_____
5. s e e i v g e h n t	two numbers	_____	_____
6. w m h o e t e o l r	two parts of a car	_____	_____

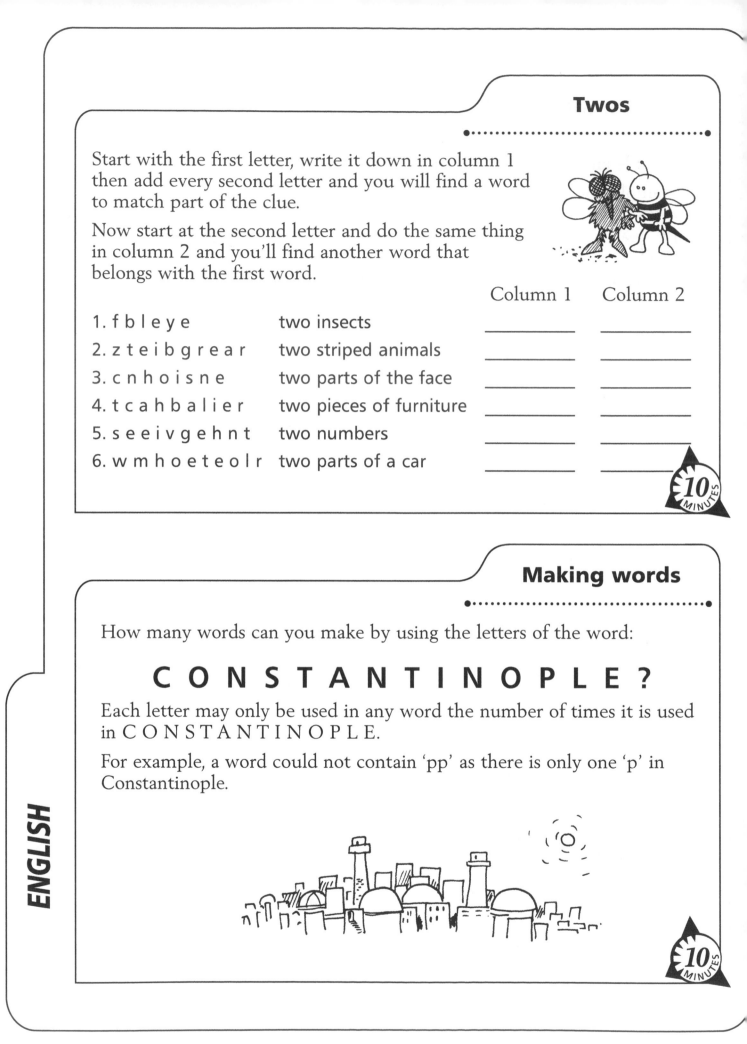

Making words

How many words can you make by using the letters of the word:

C O N S T A N T I N O P L E ?

Each letter may only be used in any word the number of times it is used in C O N S T A N T I N O P L E.

For example, a word could not contain 'pp' as there is only one 'p' in Constantinople.

ENGLISH

Small words

Find a small word in the larger word to fill the space in each sentence.
For example:

stable	I put the knife on the _____table_____ .
shamble	I ate a _____ sandwich for lunch.
problem	Be careful the thief does not _____ you!
pyjamas	I spread some strawberry _____ on the bread.
obedient	I went to _____ at nine.
cabbage	I put all the carrots in the _____ .
height	I will be _____ years old tomorrow.
furniture	I brushed my cat's smooth _____ .
haunt	My favourite _____ is visiting us next week.
hundred	We painted the walls a bright _____ .
spanner	I cooked the scrambled eggs in a _____ .

5 MINUTES

To be or not to be

All the words below begin with 'be'.
Write the full word that matches the meaning.

be _____ you sleep in it

be _____ part of a bird

be _____ an insect

be _____ under

be _____ it rings

be _____ a small fruit

be _____ hair on your face

be _____ a vegetable

be _____ a large animal

be _____ to start

5 MINUTES

ENGLISH

Brilliant Publications

This page may be reproduced by the original purchaser for non-commercial classroom use.

Timely Tasks for Fast Finishers 7–9 Year Olds

© Blake Publishing

19

Unjumble the word in brackets and add it to the word on its left to make a compound word.

rain_____ (tcoa)   **tooth**_____ (rbshu)

moon_____ (ilght)   **photo**_____ (rgaph)

life_____ (obat)   **hitch**_____ (ihker)

note_____ (bkoo)   **space**_____ (ishp)

cross_____ (rdoa)   **honey**_____ (cmbo)

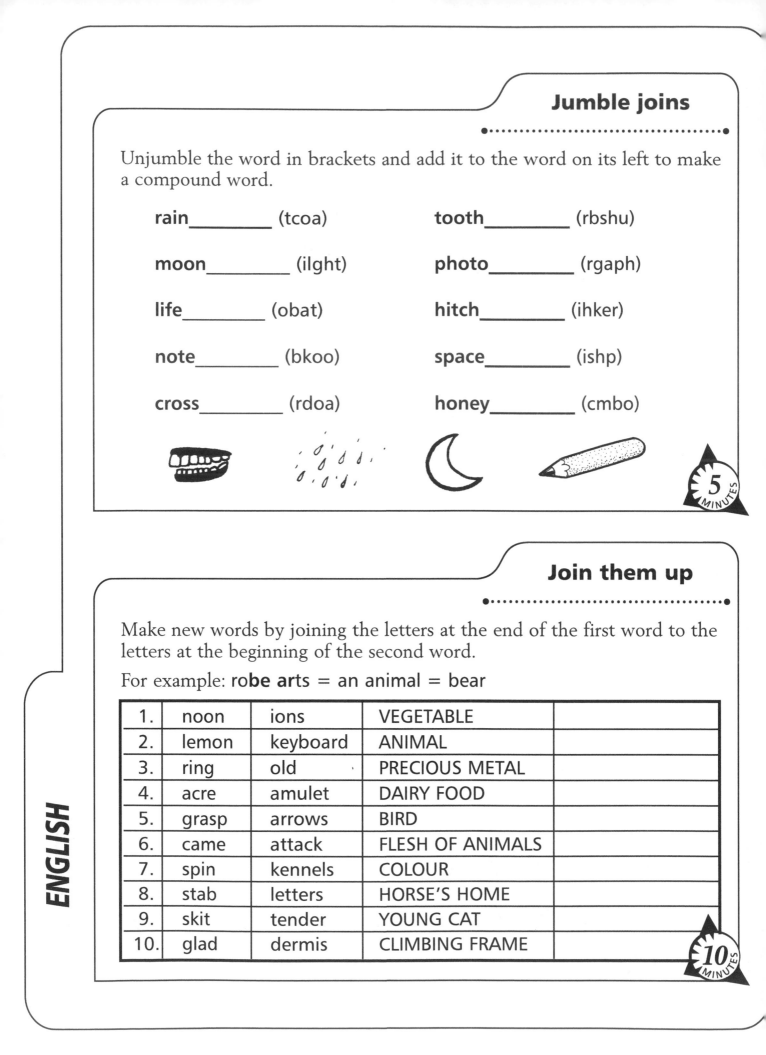

5 MINUTES

Join them up

Make new words by joining the letters at the end of the first word to the letters at the beginning of the second word.

For example: ro**be ar**ts = an animal = bear

1.	noon	ions	VEGETABLE	
2.	lemon	keyboard	ANIMAL	
3.	ring	old	PRECIOUS METAL	
4.	acre	amulet	DAIRY FOOD	
5.	grasp	arrows	BIRD	
6.	came	attack	FLESH OF ANIMALS	
7.	spin	kennels	COLOUR	
8.	stab	letters	HORSE'S HOME	
9.	skit	tender	YOUNG CAT	
10.	glad	dermis	CLIMBING FRAME	

10 MINUTES

ENGLISH

Timely Tasks for Fast Finishers 7–9 Year Olds
© Blake Publishing

Word clock

Use the word clock to make as many words as you can.

One has been done for you: heat

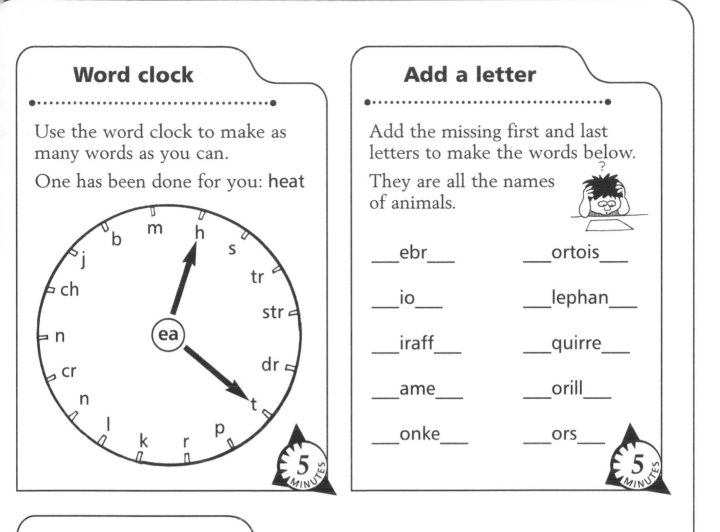

Add a letter

Add the missing first and last letters to make the words below.

They are all the names of animals.

___ebr___   ___ortois___

___io___   ___lephan___

___iraff___   ___quirre___

___ame___   ___orill___

___onke___   ___ors___

Which letter?

In the words 'must', 'thrash', 'team', 'pester' and 'steam', the only letter that appears in every word is 't'.

Write down the letter that appears in each of the words in the following groups.

1.	coast	roast	must	team	stoat	
2.	pair	pear	ripe	peer	rare	
3.	union	ruthless	purse	pull	gruel	
4.	easily	trees	easel	Easter	pea	
5.	dawn	wheel	wealth	drawn	prawn	
6.	smooth	mouth	might	mostly	moon	

Write the letters in this column.

ENGLISH

Brilliant Publications

This page may be reproduced by the original purchaser for non-commercial classroom use.

Timely Tasks for Fast Finishers 7–9 Year Olds

© Blake Publishing

21

Look at the words in the box then answer the questions.

rainbow	write	eleven	thorough	cauliflower

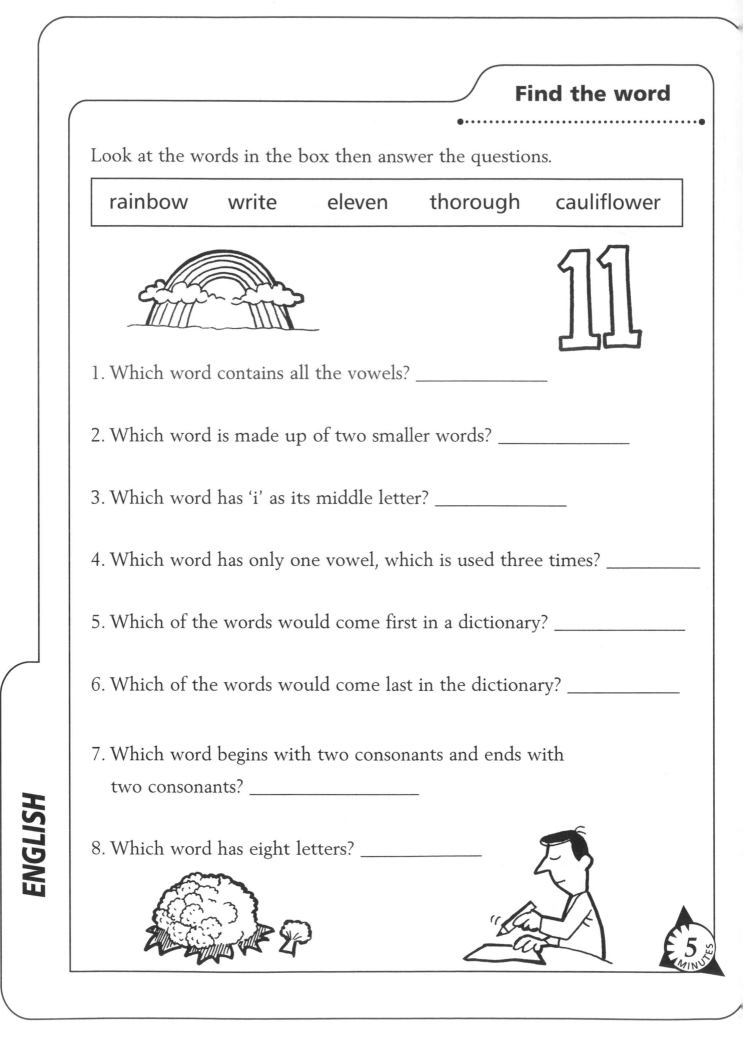

1. Which word contains all the vowels? _____

2. Which word is made up of two smaller words? _____

3. Which word has 'i' as its middle letter? _____

4. Which word has only one vowel, which is used three times? _____

5. Which of the words would come first in a dictionary? _____

6. Which of the words would come last in the dictionary? _____

7. Which word begins with two consonants and ends with
   two consonants? _____

8. Which word has eight letters? _____

ENGLISH

5 MINUTES

Brilliant Publications

Timely Tasks for Fast Finishers 7–9 Year Olds
© Blake Publishing

Picture puzzle

Write the name of each object across each row in the grid below.

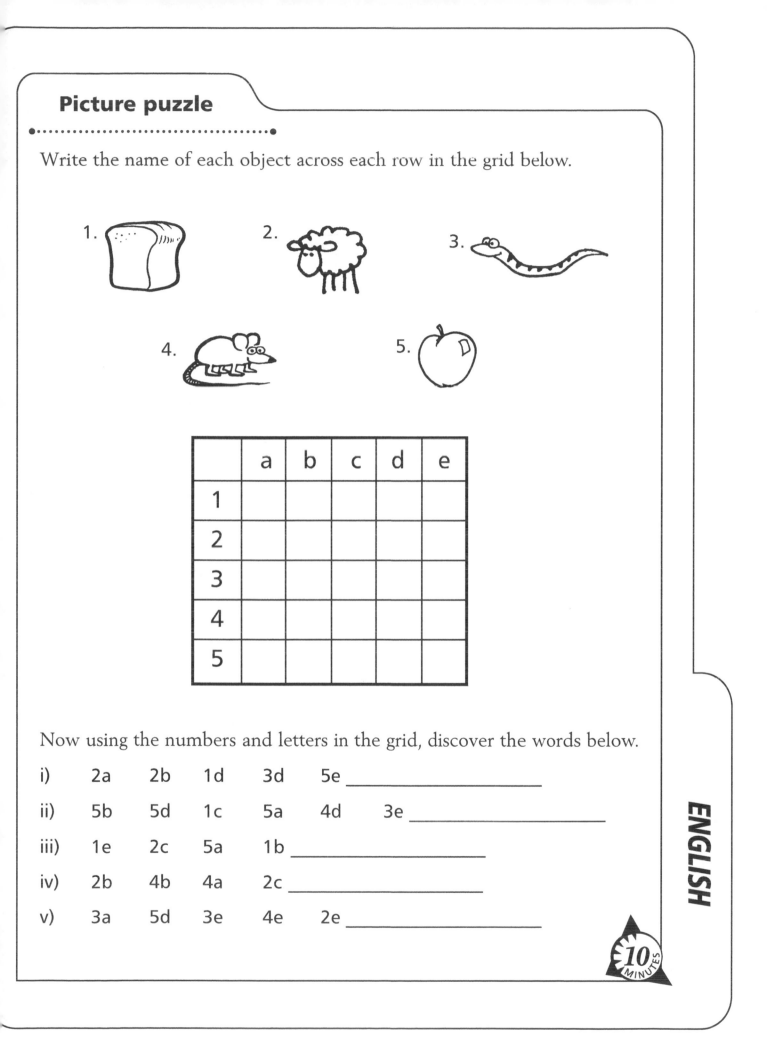

1.

2.

3.

4.

5.

	a	b	c	d	e
1					
2					
3					
4					
5					

Now using the numbers and letters in the grid, discover the words below.

i)   2a   2b   1d   3d   5e _____

ii)   5b   5d   1c   5a   4d   3e _____

iii) 1e   2c   5a   1b _____

iv)   2b   4b   4a   2c _____

v)   3a   5d   3e   4e   2e _____

ENGLISH

Brilliant Publications

This page may be reproduced by the original purchaser for non-commercial classroom use.

Timely Tasks for Fast Finishers 7–9 Year Olds

© Blake Publishing

23

Pattern puzzle

Find the pattern relating the first two rows of numbers in the tables to the bottom row.

Then complete each table.

1.

4	9	8	7	9	11	15	16	14	13	17	21	25
3	4	6	7	8	7	6	8	10	11	6	9	8
7	13											

2.

2	4	5	6	7	5	8	5	9	7	8	10	6
3	2	3	3	4	4	3	5	5	2	5	10	4
6	8											

3.

10	8	11	12	14	19	12	16	20	30	13	17	100
5	3	4	6	4	8	7	10	11	1	7	12	20
5	5											

Three's a crowd

1. Find all the 3 times table number words in the grid.

2. Colour these numbers using different colours.

f	e	l	e	v	e	n	t	w	e	l	v	e
i	t	t	w	e	n	t	y	f	o	u	r	s
f	h	t	w	e	n	t	y	o	n	e	n	e
t	i	t	h	i	r	t	e	e	n	s	i	v
e	r	t	e	n	t	h	r	e	e	i	n	e
e	t	e	i	g	h	t	e	e	n	x	e	n
n	y	t	w	e	n	t	y	s	e	v	e	n

3. Circle four numbers that are not part of the 3 times table.

MATHS

Circling around

Complete the number circles by filling in the correct numbers.

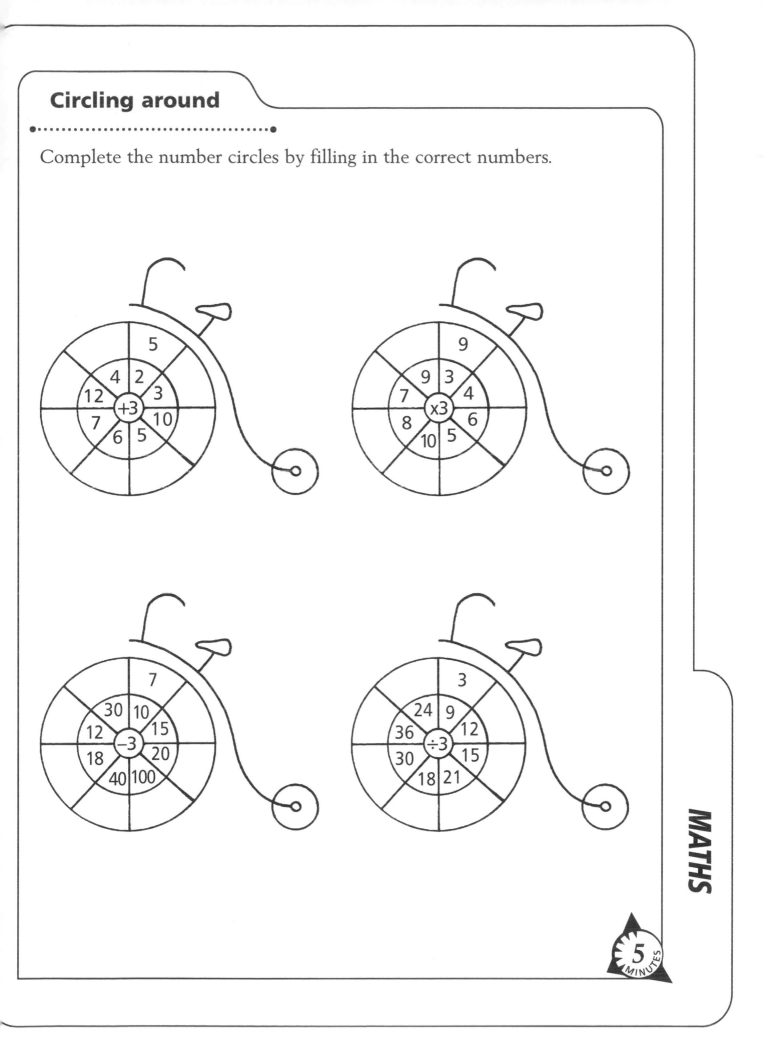

Brilliant Publications

This page may be reproduced by the original purchaser for non-commercial classroom use.

Timely Tasks for Fast Finishers 7–9 Year Olds

© Blake Publishing

25

MATHS

5 MINUTES

Work out the answers to the sums using the code below:

a stands for 2

b stands for 5

c stands for 3

$a + b + c =$ _____

$(a \times b) + c =$ _____

$(b + c) \div a =$ _____

$(a + b) \times c =$ _____

$a + b - c =$ _____

$a + (b \times c) =$ _____

$(b + c) - a =$ _____

$(a \times b) - c =$ _____

$(a \times c) - b =$ _____

$(a + b) \times c =$ _____

$b + b + b + b =$ _____

$b + b + c + c + a + a =$ _____

5 MINUTES

Number words

Cross out all the letters in the squares that have an even number beside them. Use the leftover letters to make a word that fits the definitions next to each line.

1.	a^9	e^7	s^8	z^3	r^5	p^4	b^7	striped animal _____
2.	l^9	e^{17}	a^{21}	p^{13}	m^8	p^7	n^{12}	fruit _____
3.	r^{17}	x^{14}	b^{11}	t^{100}	o^{15}	m^{21}	o^{27}	we sweep with it _____
4.	n^9	e^{21}	t^{20}	m^{40}	r^{25}	g^{65}	e^{73}	colour _____
5.	p^{86}	s^{17}	e^{35}	u^{41}	o^{57}	t^{14}	m^{63}	small animal _____
6.	m^{72}	r^7	t^{19}	t^{99}	e^{85}	u^{37}	b^{25}	food from milk _____

5 MINUTES

MATHS

Brilliant Publications

Timely Tasks for Fast Finishers 7–9 Year Olds
© Blake Publishing

Tables tree

Colour all the **4 times table** numbers **blue**.
Colour all the *5 times table* numbers *red*.

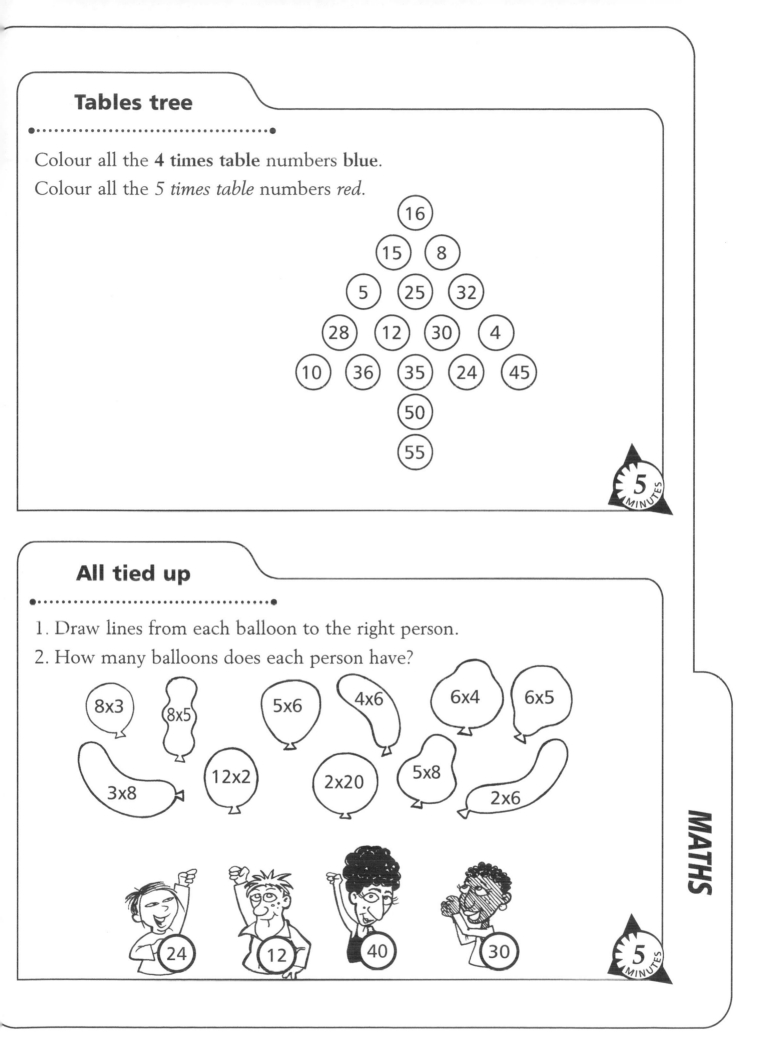

16
15 8
5 25 32
28 12 30 4
10 36 35 24 45
50
55

5 MINUTES

All tied up

1. Draw lines from each balloon to the right person.
2. How many balloons does each person have?

8x3   8x5   5x6   4x6   6x4   6x5

3x8   12x2   2x20   5x8   2x6

24   12   40   30

5 MINUTES

Brilliant Publications

This page may be reproduced by the original purchaser for non-commercial classroom use.

Timely Tasks for Fast Finishers 7–9 Year Olds
© Blake Publishing

27

MATHS

Missing numbers

Can you work out the missing number in each square?

1	2	3
4	5	
7	8	9

2	4	6
8	10	12
	16	18

3		9
12	15	18
21	24	27

28	32	36
40	44	
52	56	60

1	6	11
16		26
31	36	41

2	4	8
16		64
128	256	512

5 MINUTES

What am I?

Try to solve these number problems.

1. I am odd. I am less than 10. I am the largest single digit you can write. I am ☐.

2. I am even and I am less than 10. I am more than a pair. You can count me on one hand. I am ☐.

3. I am a number between 10 and 20. I am odd. The sum of my digits is 8. I am ☐.

4. I am more than 10 but less than 20. I am even. The sum of my digits is 9. I am ☐.

5. I am an even number between 20 and 30. I am divisible by 2, 4, 6 and 12. The sum of my digits is 6. I am ☐.

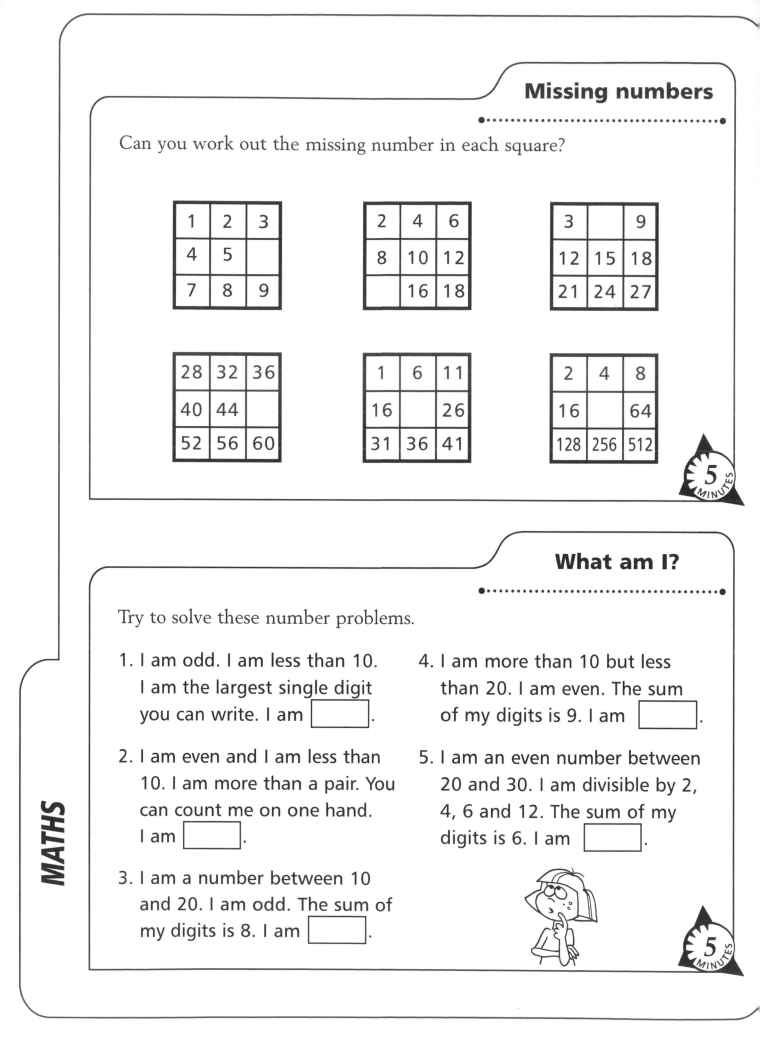

5 MINUTES

MATHS

Timely Tasks for Fast Finishers 7–9 Year Olds
© Blake Publishing

How far to go?

These insects are on their way home.

1. Use your ruler to measure the paths each has to make.
2. Who has the farthest to go?
3. Write the distances in the boxes.

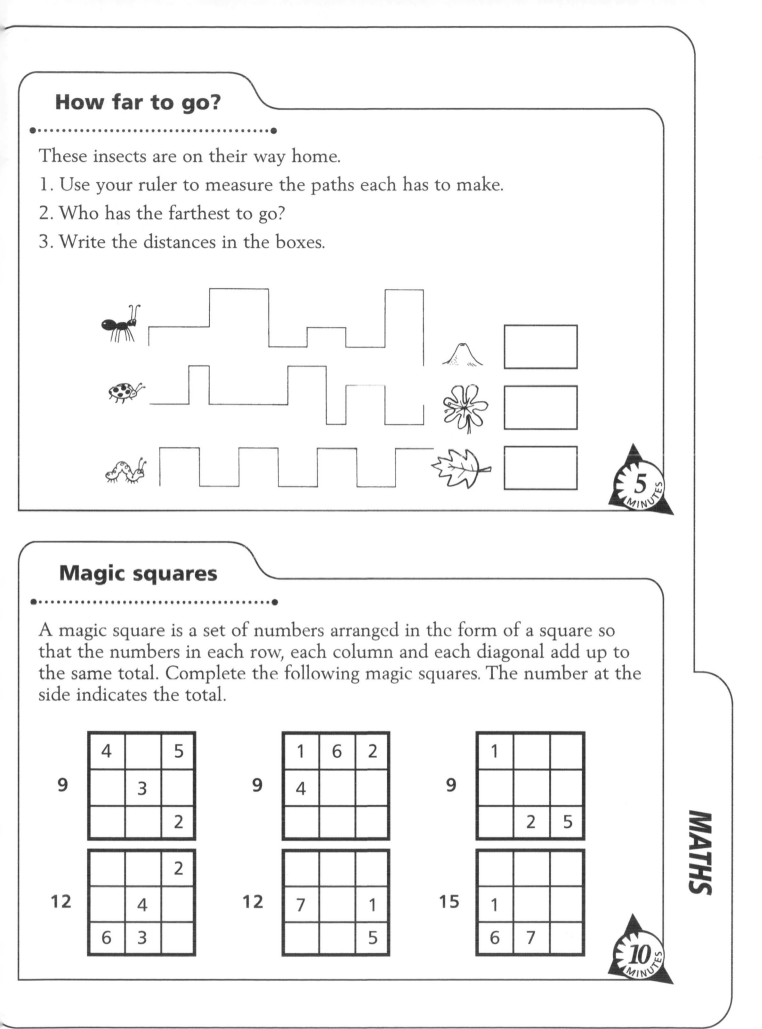

5 MINUTES

Magic squares

A magic square is a set of numbers arranged in the form of a square so that the numbers in each row, each column and each diagonal add up to the same total. Complete the following magic squares. The number at the side indicates the total.

9
4		5
	3	
		2

9
1	6	2
4		

9
1		
	2	5

12
		2
	4	
6	3	

12
7		1
		5

15
1		
6	7	

MATHS

10 MINUTES

Brilliant Publications

This page may be reproduced by the original purchaser for non-commercial classroom use.

Timely Tasks for Fast Finishers 7–9 Year Olds
© Blake Publishing

29

Read this carefully, then answer the questions.
Only Paul and Tuki eat bananas.
Only Tuki and Joanne eat grapes.
Only Paul and Joanne eat apples.

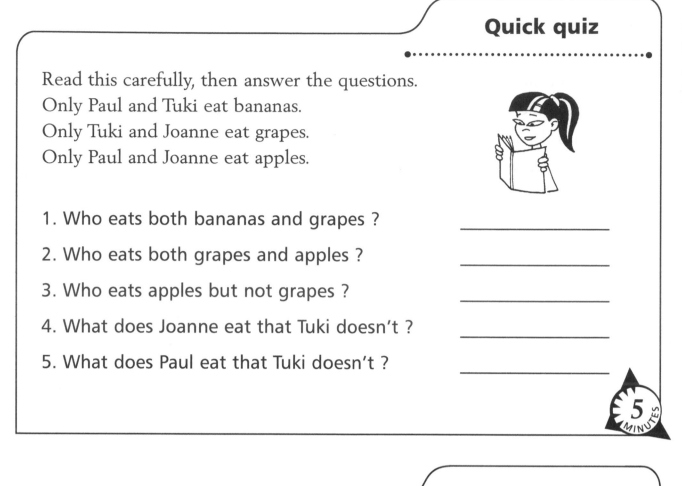

1. Who eats both bananas and grapes ? _____

2. Who eats both grapes and apples ? _____

3. Who eats apples but not grapes ? _____

4. What does Joanne eat that Tuki doesn't ? _____

5. What does Paul eat that Tuki doesn't ? _____

5 MINUTES

Codes

a	b	c	d	e	f	g	h	i	j	k	l	m	n	o	p
10	20	30	40	50	5	6	8	7	9	14	15	16	18	12	21

q	r	s	t	u	v	w	x	y	z
22	25	28	35	60	70	100	3	44	48

Using the numbers given for each letter discover the words below:

1. 10x3 3x5 4x3 3x10 7x2

_____

2. 7x4 7x5 3x4 10x7 10x5

_____

3. 20+10 6+2 5+5 4+3 20+5

_____

4. 16-2 60-10 40-5 40-5 20-5 60-10

_____

5. 3+2 20+5 30+30 4+3 30+5

_____

6. 6x5 4x2 10x5 2x25 7x4 10x5

_____

7. 7x5 5x2 5x4 5x3 10x5

_____

8. 4x2 10x5 5x2 7x5 10x5 5x5

_____

5 MINUTES

MATHS

Timely Tasks for Fast Finishers 7–9 Year Olds
© Blake Publishing

Quick calculations

Answer these as quickly as you can. See if you can get them all correct.

1. 8 + 3 + 4 =
2. 1/2 of 20 =
3. 2 x 5 =
4. 7 x 2 + 5 =
5. 20 – 2 – 2 =
6. 11 + 4 + 5 =
7. double 6 =
8. 2 x 4 + 7 =
9. 5 x 4 – 3 =
10. days in two weeks =
11. 10 x ____ = 100

12. pence in £1.65 =
13. 8 more than 16 =
14. 7 less than 16 =
15. 40 – 4 – 4 =
16. 2 x 20 + 10 =
17. odd numbers between 10 and 20 _____
18. in figures: one hundred and nine _____

Number puzzle

Complete the number puzzle. Use a calculator if you need to.

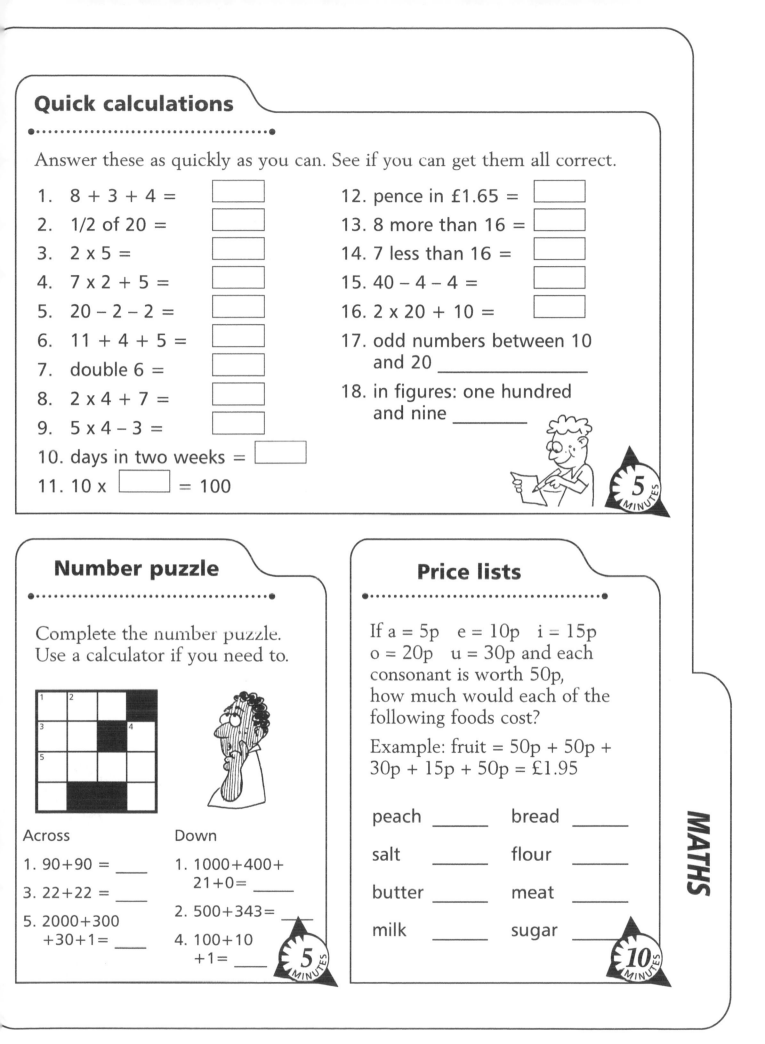

Across

1. 90+90 = ____
3. 22+22 = ____
5. 2000+300 +30+1= ____

Down

1. 1000+400+ 21+0= ____
2. 500+343= ____
4. 100+10 +1= ____

Price lists

If a = 5p   e = 10p   i = 15p o = 20p   u = 30p and each consonant is worth 50p, how much would each of the following foods cost?

Example: fruit = 50p + 50p + 30p + 15p + 50p = £1.95

peach _____   bread _____

salt _____   flour _____

butter _____   meat _____

milk _____   sugar _____

MATHS

Brilliant Publications

This page may be reproduced by the original purchaser for non-commercial classroom use.

Timely Tasks for Fast Finishers 7–9 Year Olds

© Blake Publishing

31

In each column, start with the number given, then follow the instructions to find the last number.

1.		2.		3.	
Start with 3		Start with 10		Start with 8	
Double it	☐	Halve it	☐	Double it	☐
Add 4	☐	Multiply by 3	☐	Add 20	☐
Double it	☐	Double it	☐	Subtract 5	☐
Add 10	☐	Add 20	☐	Double it	☐
Take away 5	☐	Add 30	☐	Add 8	☐
… and I am	☐	Now add 20	☐	Now double it	☐
		… and I am	☐	… and I am	☐

5 MINUTES

Class quiz

Read this carefully.

In my class there are 20 pupils and 12 of them are over 9 years old. Altogether in the class there are 12 boys, 5 of whom are over 9 years old.

1. How many girls are over 9 ? _____

2. How many girls are under 9 ? _____

3. How many boys are over 9 ? _____

4. How many boys are under 9 ? _____

5. How many girls are there in the class ? _____

6. How many more boys than girls are there in the class ? _____

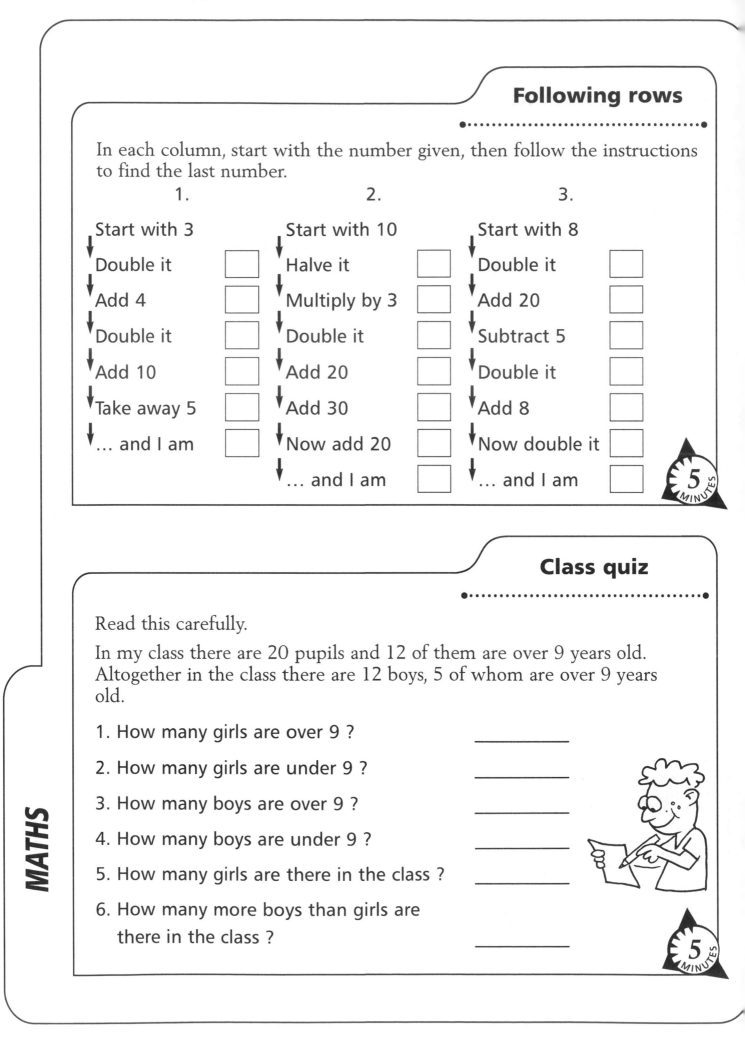

5 MINUTES

MATHS

Brilliant Publications

Timely Tasks for Fast Finishers 7–9 Year Olds
© Blake Publishing

Fruit loops

Multiply the number above each box by 3. Use your answers and the code breaker to find the fruit.

Code breaker

21	24	30	33	6	15	12	18	27	9	36	3
a	b	e	g	i	l	n	o	p	r	c	h

1. 9 10 7 3 □□□□

2. 7 9 9 5 10 □□□□□

3. 9 10 7 12 1 □□□□□

4. 8 7 4 7 4 7 □□□□□□

5. 6 3 7 4 11 10 □□□□□□

6. 11 3 7 9 10 □□□□□

5 MINUTES

Flags and poles

1. Work out the answers on each flag.
2. Find a pole that gives the same answer.
3. Draw the flag on the matching pole. The first one has been done for you.

3x4=___   10x2=___   6x5=___   6x3=___

4x4=___   8x5=___   8x3=___   10x5=___

6x5=30

| 10x3 | 2x20 | 5x4 | 2x9 | 2x6 | 2x12 | 2x25 | 2x8 |

5 MINUTES

MATHS

Brilliant Publications

This page may be reproduced by the original purchaser for non-commercial classroom use.

Timely Tasks for Fast Finishers 7–9 Year Olds

© Blake Publishing

33

Which truck in each row has the biggest load?

For each truck, work out the number facts and add their answers together. Colour the truck with the biggest total in each row.

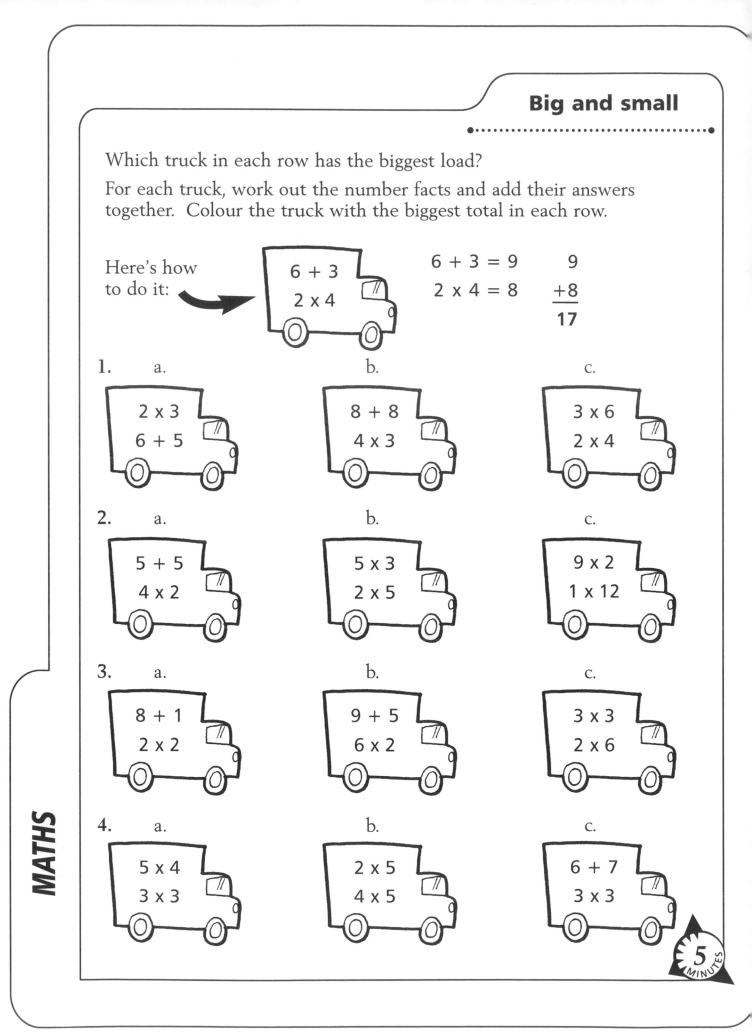

Here's how to do it:

6 + 3
2 x 4

$6 + 3 = 9$
$2 \times 4 = 8$

$\begin{array}{r} 9 \\ +8 \\ \hline 17 \end{array}$

1. a.
2 x 3
6 + 5

b.
8 + 8
4 x 3

c.
3 x 6
2 x 4

2. a.
5 + 5
4 x 2

b.
5 x 3
2 x 5

c.
9 x 2
1 x 12

3. a.
8 + 1
2 x 2

b.
9 + 5
6 x 2

c.
3 x 3
2 x 6

4. a.
5 x 4
3 x 3

b.
2 x 5
4 x 5

c.
6 + 7
3 x 3

5 MINUTES

Brilliant Publications

Timely Tasks for Fast Finishers 7–9 Year Olds
© Blake Publishing

Circle sums

Colour red the two numbers in each wheel that add up to the number in its centre.

See how quickly you can finish this quiz.

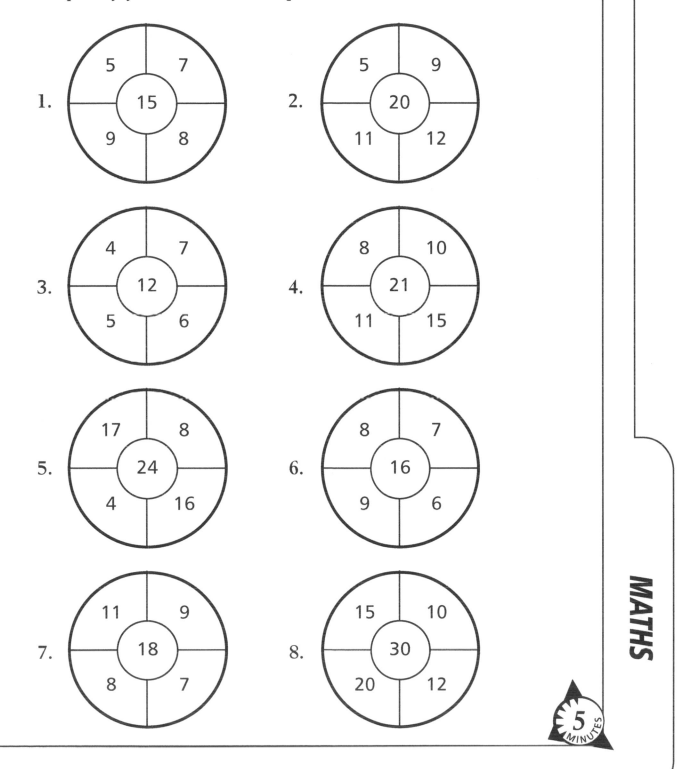

Brilliant Publications

This page may be reproduced by the original purchaser for non-commercial classroom use.

Timely Tasks for Fast Finishers 7–9 Year Olds

© Blake Publishing

MATHS

35

Work out the sums.
Colour the answers in the grid:

yellow   Double 9 = _____

red   Halve 24 = _____

pink   8 + 10 + 8 = _____

brown   40 − 5 = _____

green   2 x 10 + 13 = _____

dark blue (20 ÷ 2) + (15 ÷ 5) = _____

black   2 x 4 x 3 = _____

light blue The number that is 8 more than 17 = _____

1	2	3	4	5	6
7	8	9	10	11	12
13	14	15	16	17	18
19	20	21	22	23	24
25	26	27	28	29	30
31	32	33	34	35	36

5 MINUTES

Find the total

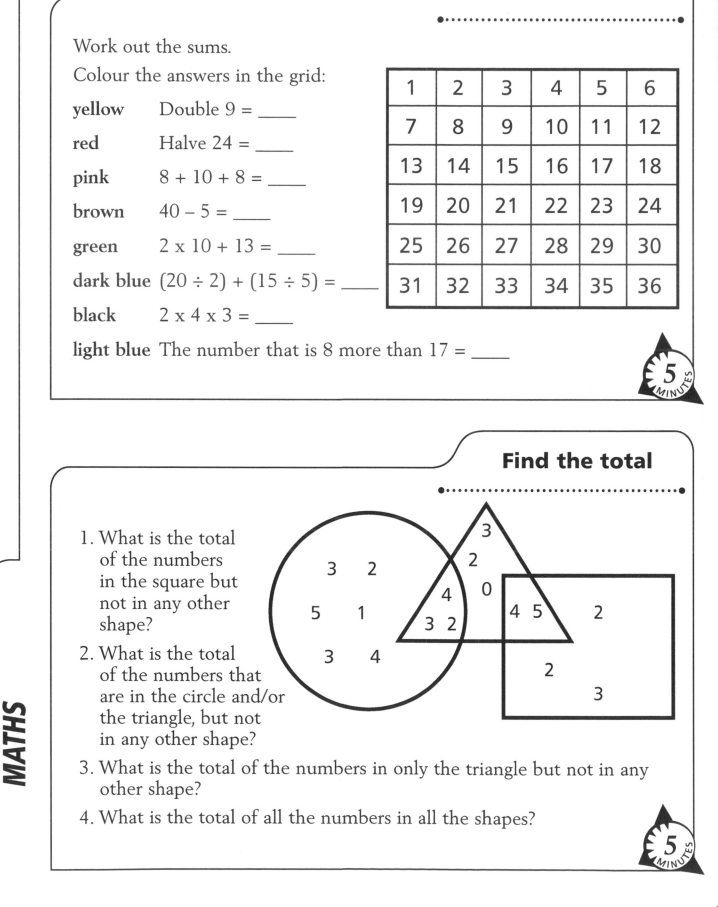

1. What is the total of the numbers in the square but not in any other shape?

2. What is the total of the numbers that are in the circle and/or the triangle, but not in any other shape?

3. What is the total of the numbers in only the triangle but not in any other shape?

4. What is the total of all the numbers in all the shapes?

5 MINUTES

MATHS

Zapping

Tony zapped four spaceships on his video game. His total score was 25.

Circle the spaceships he zapped. What other spaceships could he have zapped to score 25?

9   3   4   7

8   6   10

Tracking

Count by 3s to 60 and colour the path red.
Count by 4s to 60 and colour the path blue.

start blue   start red

7	9	11	4	3	9	12	7	3	9	18	11	14
12	13	14	6	8	12	8	6	63	6	17	21	20
8	3	7	5	9	16	5	4	36	16	9	19	18
5	11	8	7	6	20	3	2	81	17	11	12	3
60	4	32	28	24	33	2	1	64	18	15	16	1
56	3	36	9	16	94	30	27	24	21	53	61	60
52	12	40	44	18	68	33	10	7	45	48	97	57
62	48	44	71	51	13	36	39	42	61	65	51	54

MATHS

Brilliant Publications

This page may be reproduced by the original purchaser for non-commercial classroom use.

Timely Tasks for Fast Finishers 7–9 Year Olds

© Blake Publishing

37

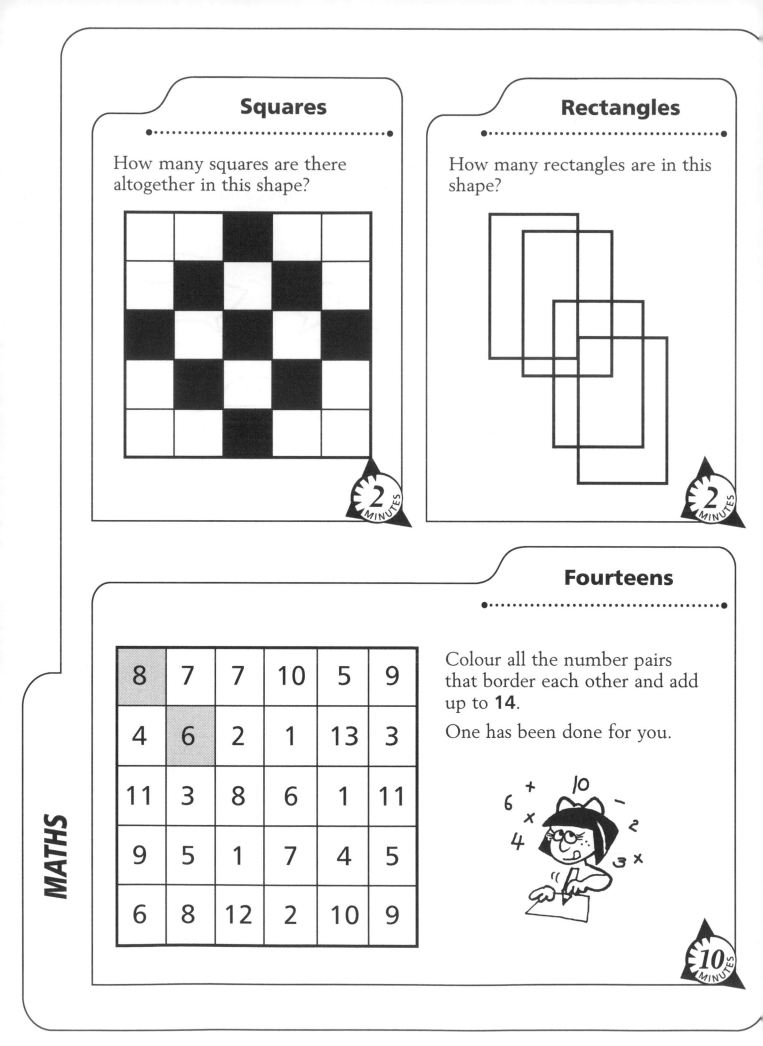

Squares

How many squares are there altogether in this shape?

2 MINUTES

Rectangles

How many rectangles are in this shape?

2 MINUTES

Fourteens

Colour all the number pairs that border each other and add up to **14**.

One has been done for you.

8	7	7	10	5	9
4	6	2	1	13	3
11	3	8	6	1	11
9	5	1	7	4	5
6	8	12	2	10	9

10 MINUTES

MATHS

Timely Tasks for Fast Finishers 7–9 Year Olds

Cubes

How many small cubes are there in this shape?

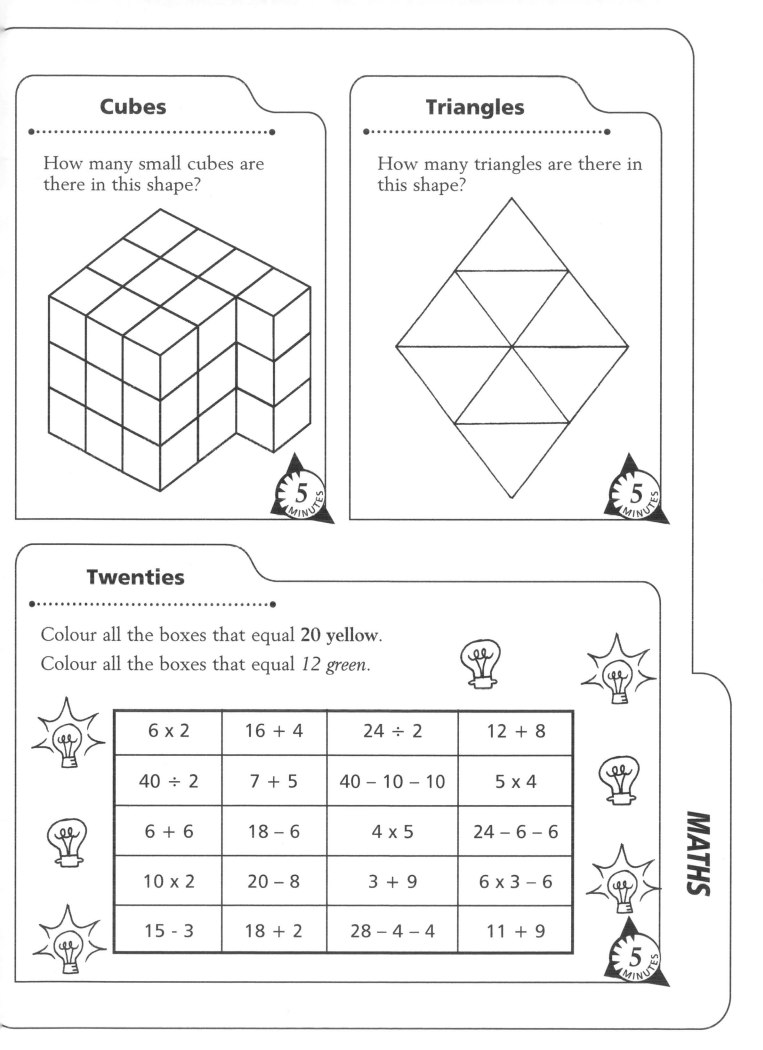

5 MINUTES

Triangles

How many triangles are there in this shape?

5 MINUTES

Twenties

Colour all the boxes that equal **20 yellow**.

Colour all the boxes that equal *12 green*.

6 x 2	16 + 4	24 ÷ 2	12 + 8
40 ÷ 2	7 + 5	40 – 10 – 10	5 x 4
6 + 6	18 – 6	4 x 5	24 – 6 – 6
10 x 2	20 – 8	3 + 9	6 x 3 – 6
15 - 3	18 + 2	28 – 4 – 4	11 + 9

5 MINUTES

MATHS

© Blake Publishing

Add the missing numbers in the square to complete each number sentence.

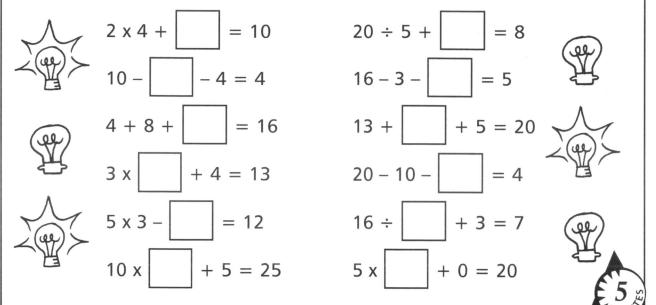

$2 \times 4 + \boxed{} = 10$

$10 - \boxed{} - 4 = 4$

$4 + 8 + \boxed{} = 16$

$3 \times \boxed{} + 4 = 13$

$5 \times 3 - \boxed{} = 12$

$10 \times \boxed{} + 5 = 25$

$20 \div 5 + \boxed{} = 8$

$16 - 3 - \boxed{} = 5$

$13 + \boxed{} + 5 = 20$

$20 - 10 - \boxed{} = 4$

$16 \div \boxed{} + 3 = 7$

$5 \times \boxed{} + 0 = 20$

5 MINUTES

Number knowledge

Look at the numbers carefully, then answer the questions.

481	563	291	692	123	39	365

1. Which is the largest of all the numbers?_____

2. Which is the smallest of all the numbers?_____

3. Which is the only even number?_____

4. Which number, plus 9, would equal 300?_____

5. Which is the largest of the odd numbers?_____

6. Which two numbers consist of exactly the same digits but in a different order?_____

7. Write all these numbers from largest to smallest.

_____

10 MINUTES

Brilliant Publications
This page may be reproduced by the original purchaser for non-commercial classroom use.

Timely Tasks for Fast Finishers 7–9 Year Olds
© Blake Publishing

MATHS

Adding squares

If ☐ = 3, what are the following shapes worth?
The first one has been done for you.

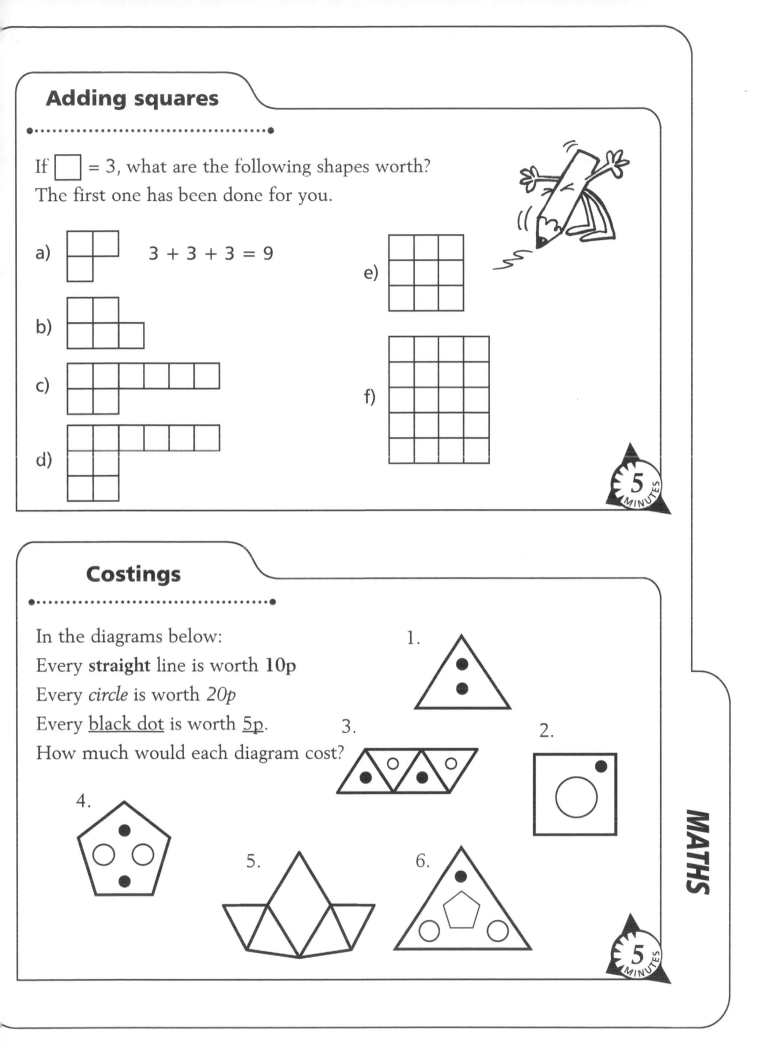

a)   3 + 3 + 3 = 9

b)

c)

d)

e)

f)

Costings

In the diagrams below:
Every **straight** line is worth **10p**
Every *circle* is worth *20p*
Every <u>black dot</u> is worth <u>5p</u>.
How much would each diagram cost?

1.

3.

2.

4.

5.

6.

Think about the relationship between the first two numbers.

What number will make the last two numbers relate to each other in the same way?

Circle the number and write it in the box.

The first one has been done for you.

1. $\boxed{5}$ is to $\boxed{10}$ as 4 is to $\boxed{8}$. (3 ⑧ 4 2)

2. $\boxed{3}$ is to $\boxed{5}$ as 7 is to $\boxed{}$. (6 5 0 9)

3. $\boxed{4}$ is to $\boxed{7}$ as 3 is to $\boxed{}$. (3 6 9 5)

4. $\boxed{3}$ is to $\boxed{8}$ as 5 is to $\boxed{}$. (7 10 12 6)

5. $\boxed{10}$ is to $\boxed{20}$ as 8 is to $\boxed{}$. (14 16 12 9)

6. $\boxed{10}$ is to $\boxed{7}$ as 6 is to $\boxed{}$. (4 3 8 5)

5 MINUTES

Fishy tales

Alex catches fish that have an **odd** number for their answer.
<u>Nina</u> catches fish that have an <u>even</u> number for their answer.
Colour the fish using blue for Nina and red for Alex
to show who catches which fish.

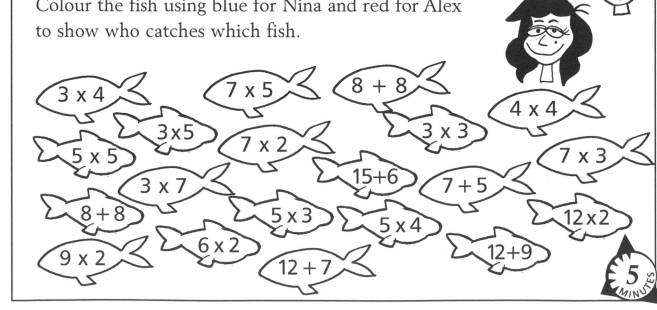

3 x 4   7 x 5   8 + 8   4 x 4
3 x 5   3 x 3
5 x 5   7 x 2   7 x 3
3 x 7   15 + 6   7 + 5
8 + 8   5 x 3   5 x 4   12 x 2
9 x 2   6 x 2   12 + 9
12 + 7

5 MINUTES

MATHS

Brilliant Publications

Timely Tasks for Fast Finishers 7–9 Year Olds
© Blake Publishing

Letters and numbers

Under each letter in the box is the number it represents.

T	B	N	Y	U	P	E	O	I	A	D
5	10	3	7	6	1	4	9	8	2	0

1. Which number represents the fifth letter in the row? ___

2. What is the total of the numbers that represent the vowels? ___

3. What is the total of the numbers that represent the letters of the word BEAN? ___

4. What number represents the middle letter of the row? ___

5. Add up the total of the numbers that represent the consonants and take it away from the total of the numbers that represent the vowels. ___

6. What words are represented by each of these number groups?

a	10	2	10	7
b	1	2	8	0
c	0	4	2	0
d	5	9	2	0

10 MINUTES

Correct boxes

Colour only those boxes that have the correct answers.

11 + 4 = 16	4 + 8 + 3 = 15	17 + 4 = 22	(3 x 6) – 2 = 16
6 + 8 + 9 = 23	20 ÷ 5 = 4	11 + 11 + 4 = 26	(10 ÷ 2) + 11 = 16
(3 x 2) + 9 = 15	15 – 3 = 10	30 – 2 – 2 = 26	5 x 5 = 26
12 – 7 = 3	8 + 3 + 7 = 18	(10 x 2) + 10 = 30	14 + 6 + 8 = 28
20 – 3 – 6 = 11	18 – 2 – 5 = 13	99 + 2 = 104	28 – 3 – 3 = 22
19 – 6 = 14	9 + 11 + 5 = 25	3 x 2 x 2 = 12	(10 x 10) + 10 = 110

5 MINUTES

MATHS

Brilliant Publications

This page may be reproduced by the original purchaser for non-commercial classroom use.

Timely Tasks for Fast Finishers 7–9 Year Olds

© Blake Publishing

43

Create patterns of your own in the grids below. Think carefully and try to make yours different from your classmates'. One has been started to give you an idea.

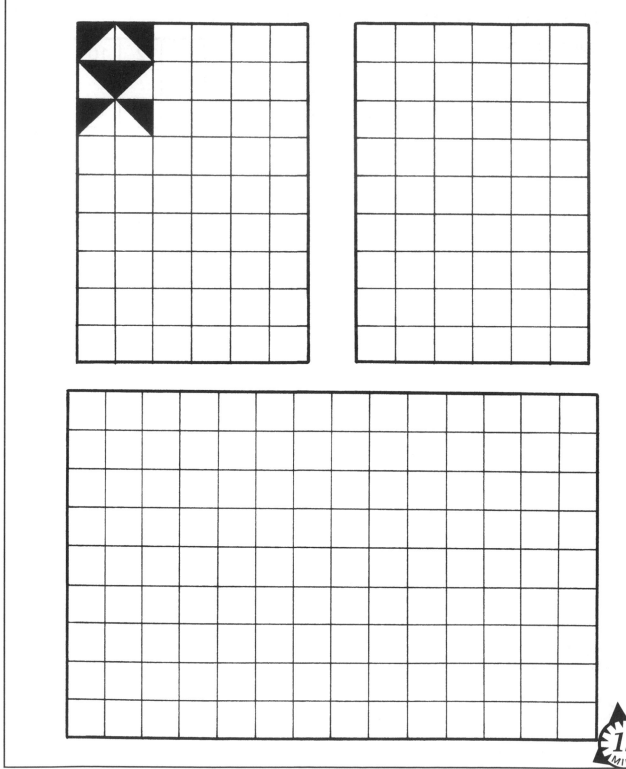

THINKING

Brilliant Publications

Timely Tasks for Fast Finishers 7–9 Year Olds

© Blake Publishing

15 MINUTES

Colour by design

Colour the design using only four colours. No shapes of the same colour should touch each other.

Pattern colour

Colour the pattern any way you wish to create an attractive design.

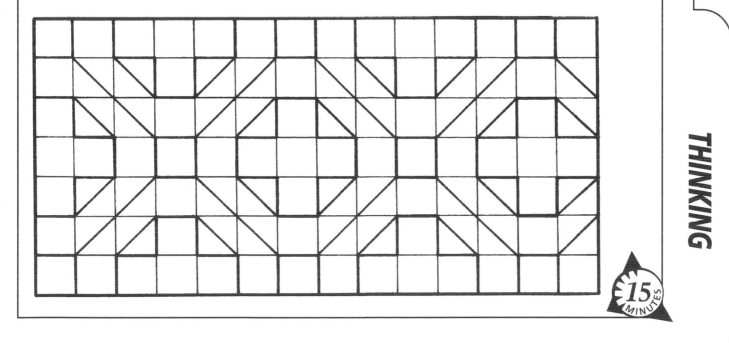

THINKING

Brilliant Publications

This page may be reproduced by the original purchaser for non-commercial classroom use.

Timely Tasks for Fast Finishers 7–9 Year Olds
© Blake Publishing

45

Look carefully at the two pictures. There are five lines missing from the second picture.

Rule in the missing lines. Now colour both pictures.

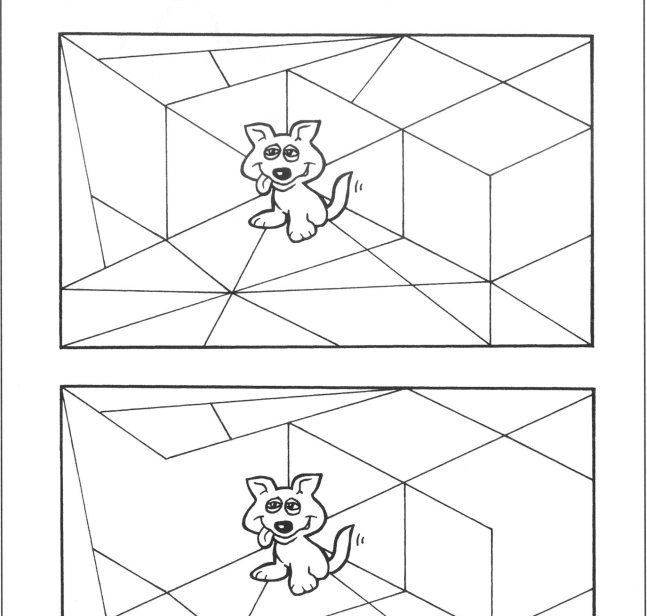

THINKING

© Blake Publishing

Shaping up

Match the picture outlines that belong together. Each of those marked 1 to 5 belongs with one of those marked A to E.

Memory test

Look closely at the ten pictures in the box below. Give yourself two minutes to look, then cover them up and write down all those you can remember.

THINKING

Brilliant Publications

This page may be reproduced by the original purchaser for non-commercial classroom use.

Timely Tasks for Fast Finishers 7–9 Year Olds

© Blake Publishing

47

You can create a very attractive pattern by following the steps below:

• rule a line from 1 to every other number

• repeat this starting at 2, then at 3 and so on.

Use a sharp lead pencil.

We have started it for you.

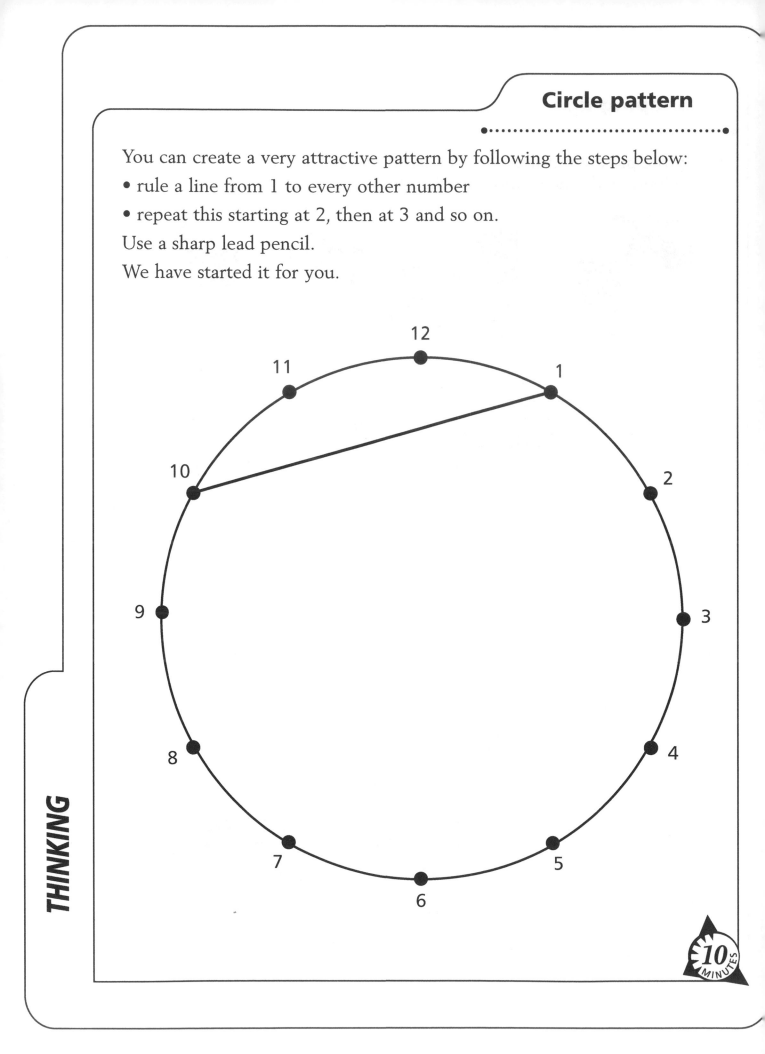

Growing larger

Look at the picture in the small grid. Using the squares to help you, draw it again in the larger grid below. Colour your picture.

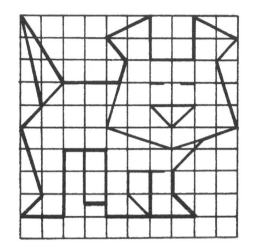

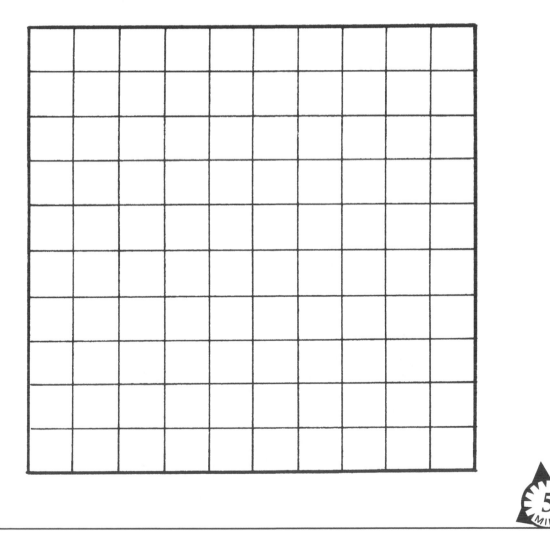

Brilliant Publications

Timely Tasks for Fast Finishers 7–9 Year Olds
© Blake Publishing

Cut out the pictures in the squares below and place them in the grid so that they make a bird. Glue them in place, and colour the picture.

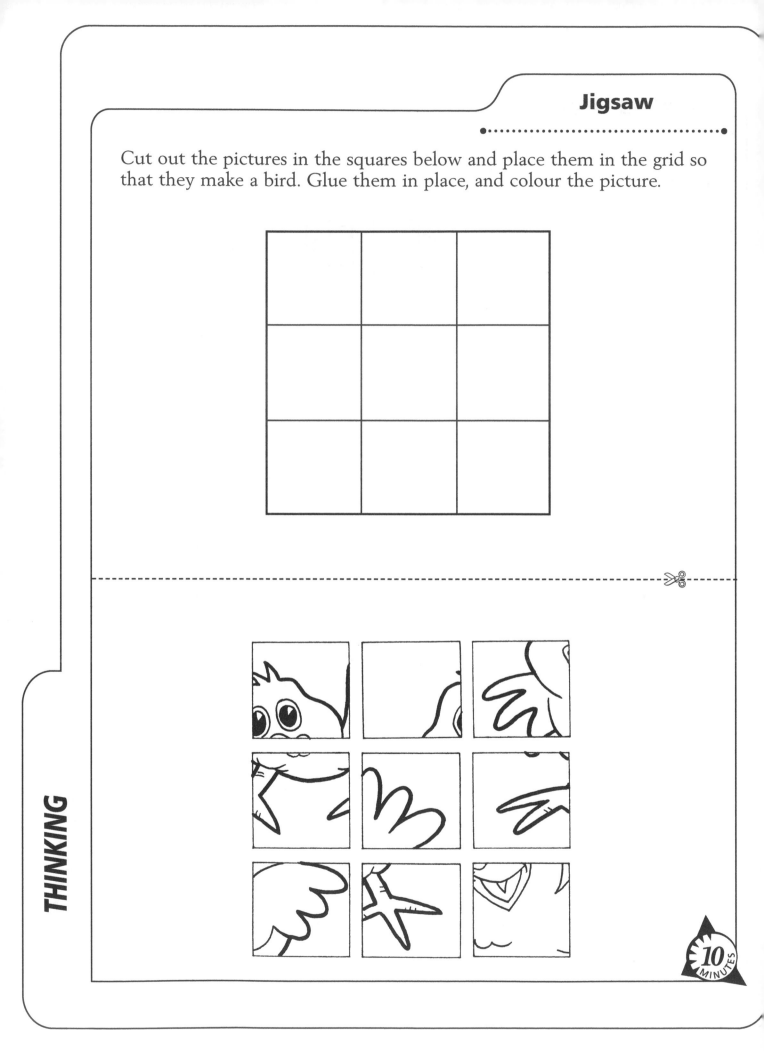

THINKING

Timely Tasks for Fast Finishers 7–9 Year Olds

© Blake Publishing

Which one is different?

Study each row of pictures. Circle the one that is different from the others in that row.

Look and think

Which group, A B or C, includes all the pieces that make the full steam train?

A

B

C

THINKING

Brilliant Publications

This page may be reproduced by the original purchaser for non-commercial classroom use.

Timely Tasks for Fast Finishers 7–9 Year Olds

© Blake Publishing

51

Squaring up

If you cut this figure into two parts using one straight line, you can then arrange the two pieces to make a square.

How would you do it?

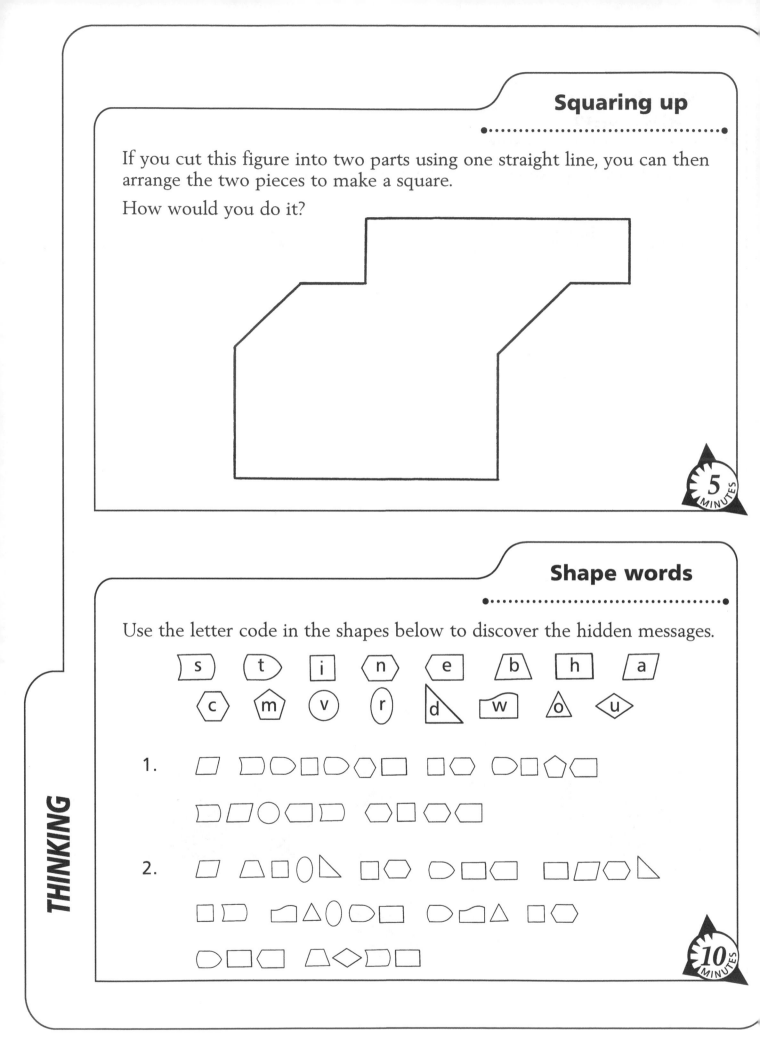

5 MINUTES

Shape words

Use the letter code in the shapes below to discover the hidden messages.

s   t   i   n   e   b   h   a
c   m   v   r   d   w   o   u

1.

2.

10 MINUTES

THINKING

Brilliant Publications

It will amaze you

Find a path through the maze. Trace the path using a lead pencil then colour the path in a bright colour. Use another colour to fill in the rest of the maze.

Remember, one way to solve a maze is to colour all the dead ends first.

Eye tricks

Colour in the missing piece from this puzzle.

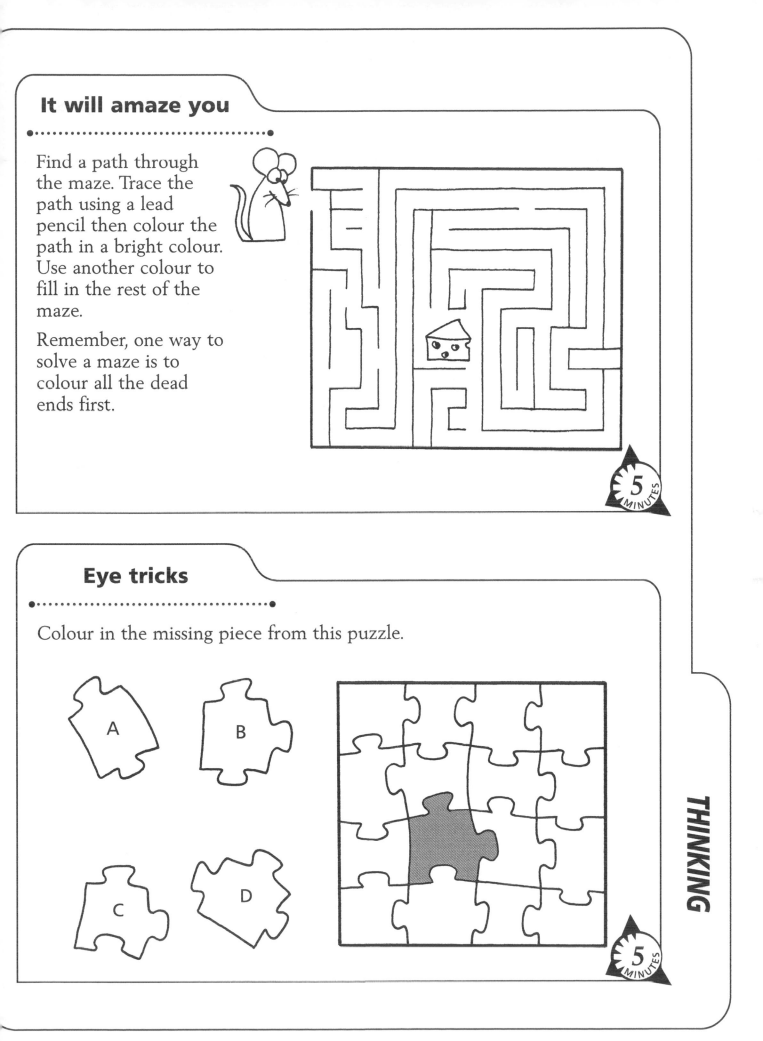

THINKING

Brilliant Publications

This page may be reproduced by the original purchaser for non-commercial classroom use.

Timely Tasks for Fast Finishers 7–9 Year Olds
© Blake Publishing

53

Tricky triangles

Colour in the triangles to form a pattern. There is no right or wrong way.

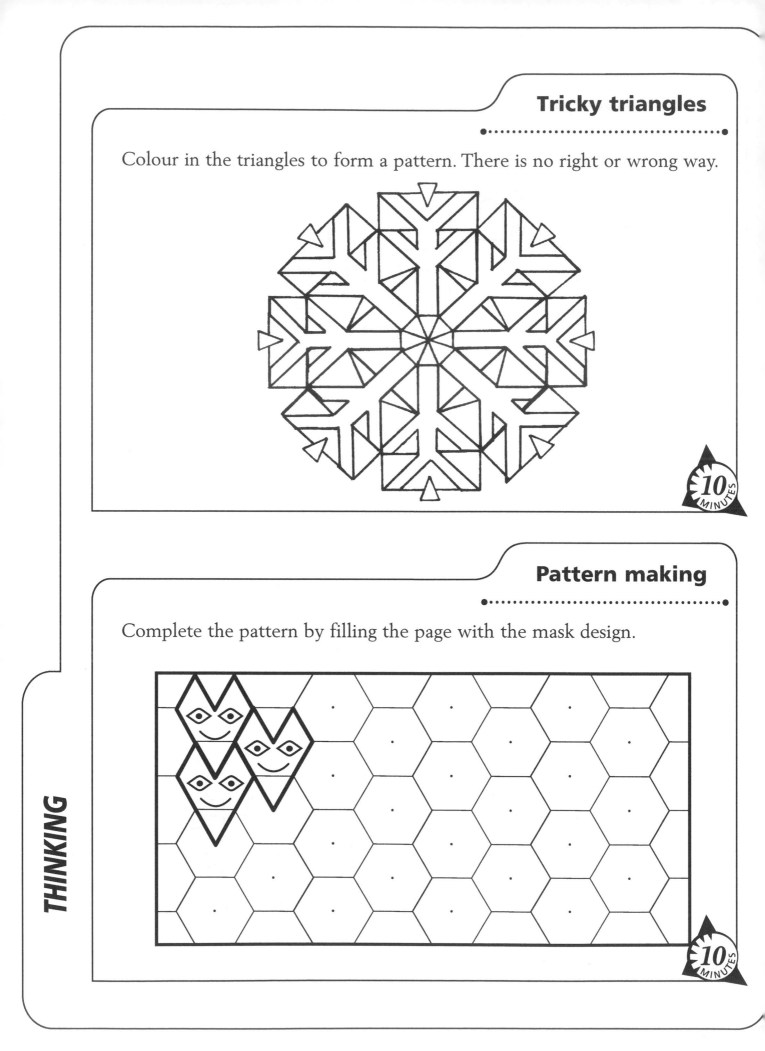

Pattern making

Complete the pattern by filling the page with the mask design.

THINKING

Brilliant Publications
Timely Tasks for Fast Finishers 7–9 Year Olds

Shadows

Unscramble the names in the box below to identify the creatures shown in silhouette. Write the names correctly under each picture.

tanagronu	cleam	coocatok	krash	yenomk
rerquils	wol	shoocnerri	agonakro	neask

Brilliant Publications

This page may be reproduced by the original purchaser for non-commercial classroom use.

Timely Tasks for Fast Finishers 7–9 Year Olds
© Blake Publishing

55

Spot the error

Can you find the mistake in each picture? Circle each one.

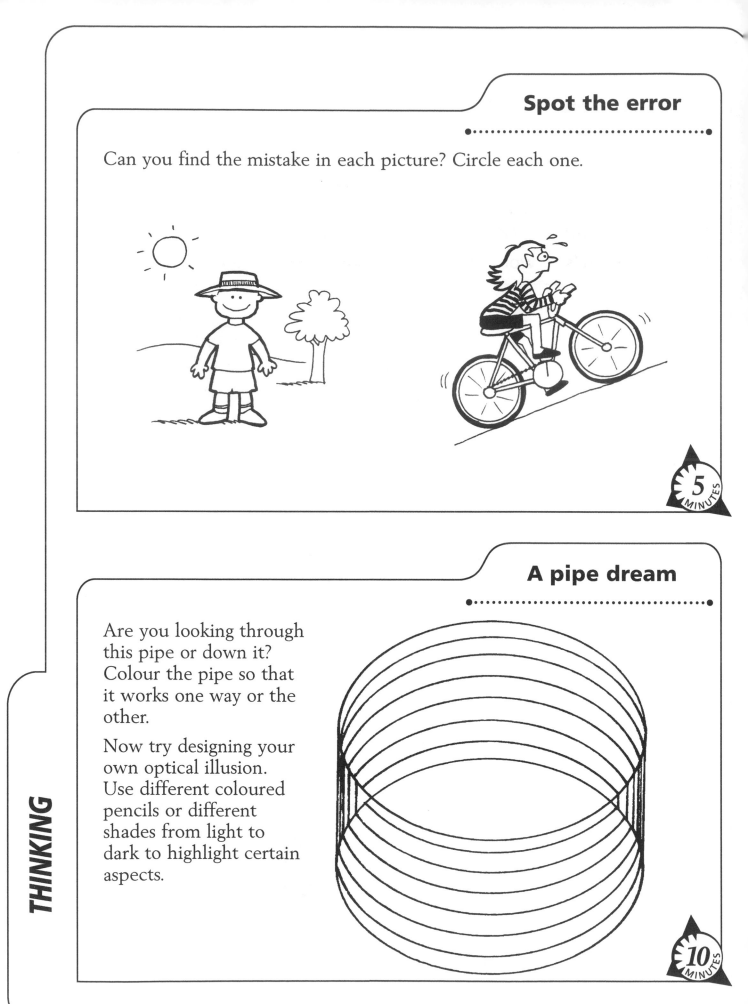

5 MINUTES

A pipe dream

Are you looking through this pipe or down it? Colour the pipe so that it works one way or the other.

Now try designing your own optical illusion. Use different coloured pencils or different shades from light to dark to highlight certain aspects.

10 MINUTES

Brilliant Publications

Timely Tasks for Fast Finishers 7–9 Year Olds
© Blake Publishing

Colour a pattern

Colour the shapes below in any way you wish to create an interesting effect. There is no right or wrong way.

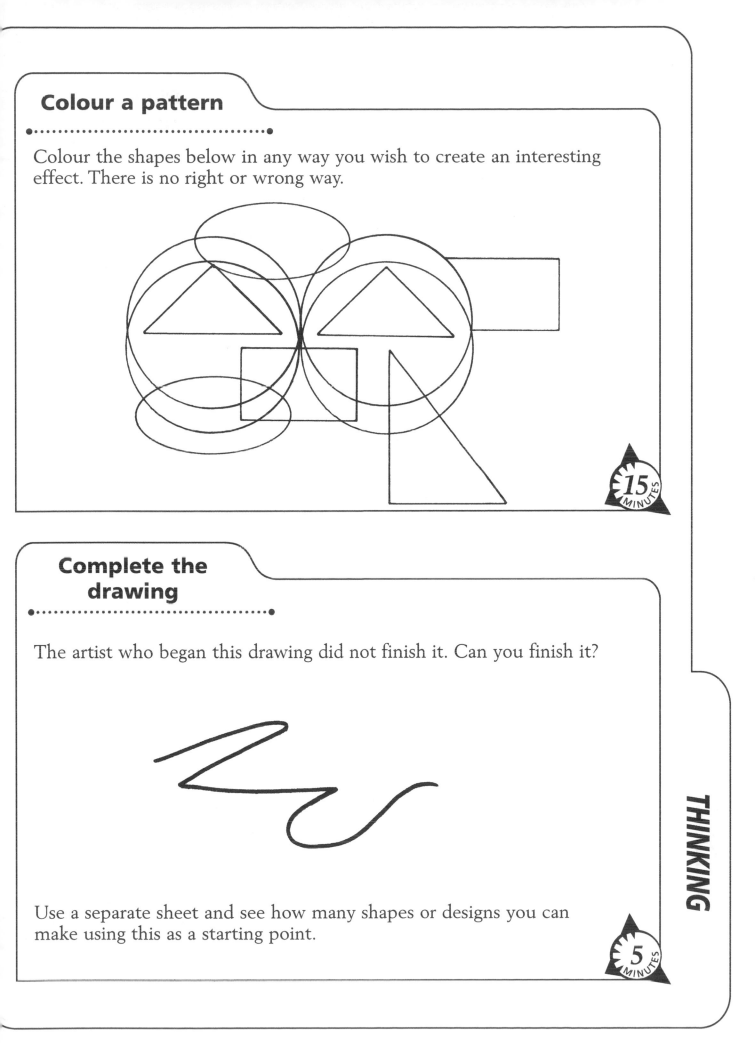

15 MINUTES

Complete the drawing

The artist who began this drawing did not finish it. Can you finish it?

Use a separate sheet and see how many shapes or designs you can make using this as a starting point.

5 MINUTES

THINKING

Brilliant Publications

This page may be reproduced by the original purchaser for non-commercial classroom use.

Timely Tasks for Fast Finishers 7–9 Year Olds
© Blake Publishing

57

Moving with air

In the box draw a bicycle that could move by using the force of the wind. Then explain how your bicycle would work.

Explanation:

_____

_____

_____

_____

_____

Use another sheet if you need more space.

10 MINUTES

Colour wheel

Colour one part of the wheel red, another blue and another yellow.

Cut out the wheel and stick it on a piece of card the same shape.

Now push a drawing pin through the centre so you can pin it loosely to a notice board. Spin the wheel quickly—what colours do you see?

5 MINUTES

SCIENCE

Blow it

Cut out the shape below. Fold it as shown in the diagram. Now blow it gently.

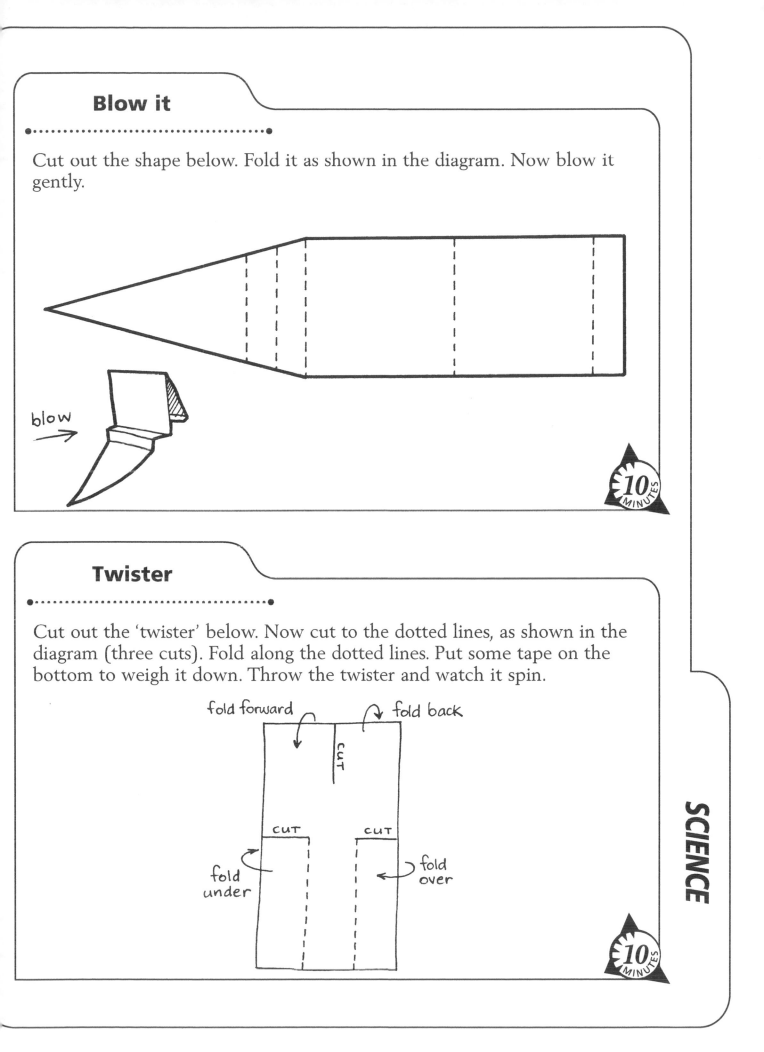

Twister

Cut out the 'twister' below. Now cut to the dotted lines, as shown in the diagram (three cuts). Fold along the dotted lines. Put some tape on the bottom to weigh it down. Throw the twister and watch it spin.

SCIENCE

Brilliant Publications

This page may be reproduced by the original purchaser for non-commercial classroom use.

Timely Tasks for Fast Finishers 7–9 Year Olds

© Blake Publishing

59

In the boxes below, name some things that get their energy from the following sources.

Electricity mains Electric battery Wind

Petrol Sunlight Food

Brilliant Publications

Timely Tasks for Fast Finishers 7–9 Year Olds

© Blake Publishing

SCIENCE

Living things

Find the names of the living things in the grid. Write them under the correct heading.

c	h	a	d	d	o	c	k	a
c	r	o	c	o	d	i	l	e
a	w	a	s	p	r	l	e	s
p	e	n	g	u	i	n	a	p
l	i	o	n	g	b	i	g	a
i	c	g	a	w	y	c	l	r
z	r	t	b	a	d	g	e	r
a	o	l	i	z	a	r	d	o
r	b	e	e	t	l	e	o	w

Mammals
1 _____
2 _____
3 _____

Reptiles
1 _____
2 _____
3 _____

Birds
1 _____
2 _____
3 _____

Insects
1 _____
2 _____
3 _____

You will also find the name of a fish.
What is it? _____

10 MINUTES

Water cycle

Colour the picture of the 'Water Cycle' and explain what is happening.

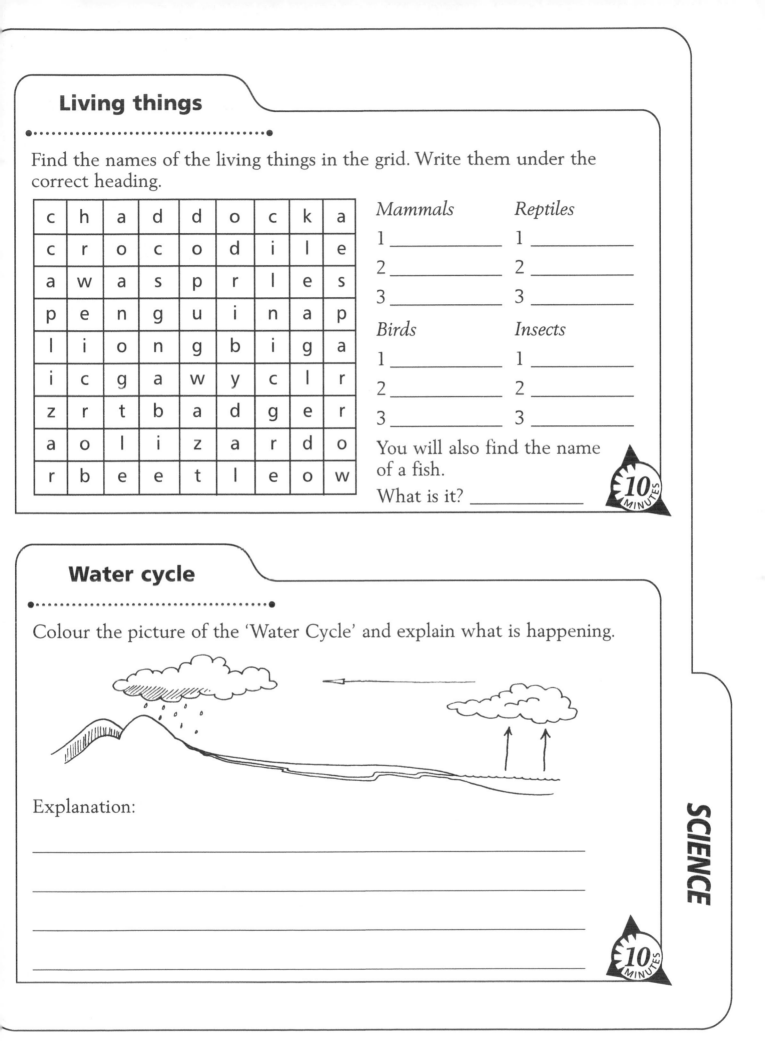

Explanation:

_____

_____

_____

_____

10 MINUTES

SCIENCE

Brilliant Publications

This page may be reproduced by the original purchaser for non-commercial classroom use.

Timely Tasks for Fast Finishers 7–9 Year Olds
© Blake Publishing

61

Choose an animal that has been introduced into Britain and is now a pest. Describe what damage it is doing to our environment.

_____

_____

_____

Suggest ways it could be controlled.

_____

_____

_____

Explain the error

Look closely at each picture below. Draw a circle around the mistake in each one. Then on a separate sheet explain why the pictures are wrong.

Brilliant Publications

Timely Tasks for Fast Finishers 7–9 Year Olds
© Blake Publishing

SCIENCE

Wordsearch

Find as many words as you can in the grid. Draw sketches of five of the things you find.

d	s	c	a	s	t	l	e	d
m	a	p	l	g	n	e	t	d
s	c	r	e	o	s	h	r	a
w	o	p	g	a	g	w	e	m
o	u	a	e	i	r	o	a	s
r	r	s	n	h	o	r	s	e
d	a	k	d	r	g	n	u	l
c	g	a	r	m	o	u	r	t
l	e	b	a	t	t	l	e	b

Use an extra sheet if you need more space.

5 MINUTES

Colour in

Colour in the picture using the earthy colours used by some Aboriginal artists.

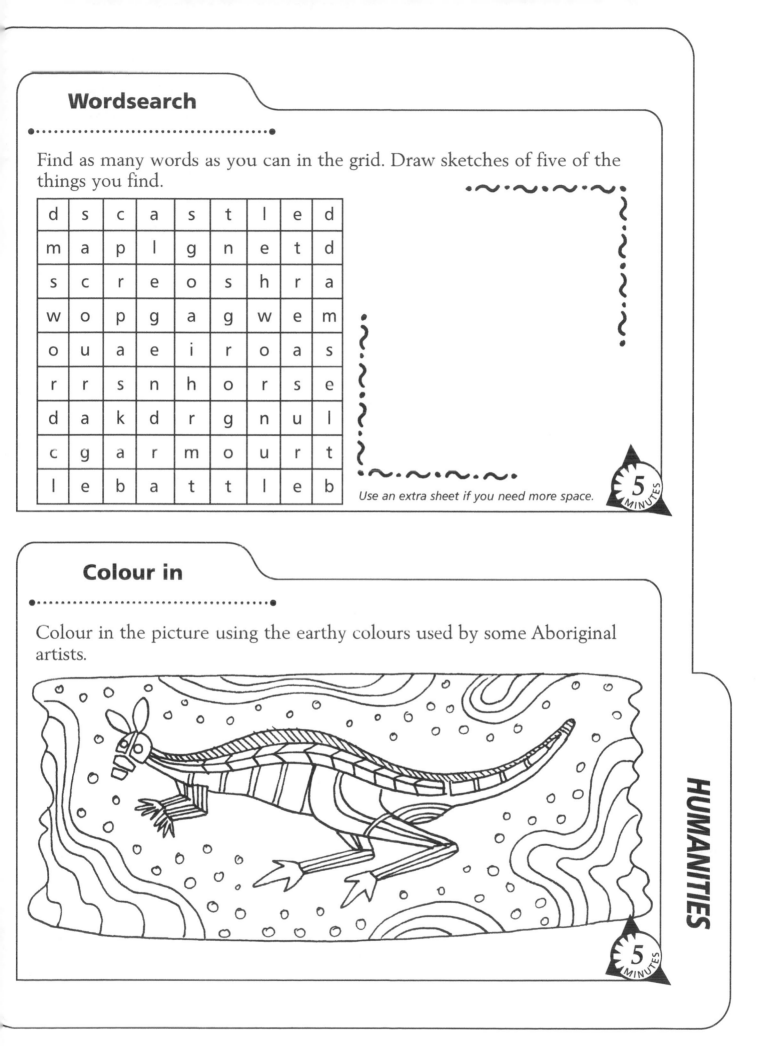

5 MINUTES

HUMANITIES

Brilliant Publications

This page may be reproduced by the original purchaser for non-commercial classroom use.

Timely Tasks for Fast Finishers 7–9 Year Olds

© Blake Publishing

63

••••••••••••••• Timely Tasks for Fast Finishers 7–9 Year Olds •••••••••••••••

Draw a line from the occupation to the service provided.

1. A baker	makes things out of wood.
2. A police officer	cares for sick or injured animals.
3. A teacher	makes bread, cakes and pies.
4. A carpenter	repairs cars.
5. A veterinary surgeon	maintains the law.
6. A chemist	helps people learn skills.
7. A hairdresser	dispenses medicines.
8. A mechanic	cuts and cares for people's hair.

Draw a picture of what you want to be when you leave school.

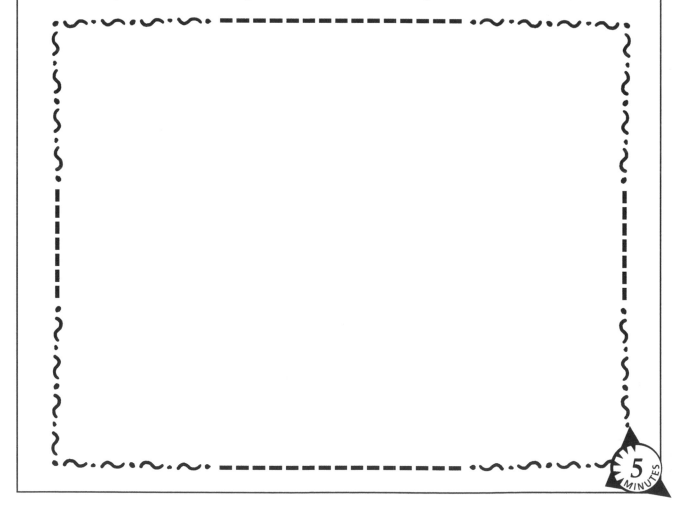

HUMANITIES

Brilliant Publications

This page may be reproduced by the original purchaser for non-commercial classroom use.

Timely Tasks for Fast Finishers 7–9 Year Olds

© Blake Publishing

Rules

Look at the pictures below. Under each picture write who you think makes up the rules for the activity shown. Then write who you think sees that the rules are obeyed.

make(s) the rules	make(s) the rules	make(s) the rules	make(s) the rules
see(s) the rules are obeyed	see(s) the rules are obeyed	see(s) the rules are obeyed	see(s) the rules are obeyed

10 MINUTES

In the past

Each picture shows something that was used in the past. In the box beside each one, draw a picture of what we might use today in its place.

5 MINUTES

HUMANITIES

Brilliant Publications

This page may be reproduced by the original purchaser for non-commercial classroom use.

Timely Tasks for Fast Finishers 7–9 Year Olds

© Blake Publishing

65

Television

15 MINUTES

Find out from your classmates what their favourite types of television show are.

Put a tick in a box for the number of students who like a particular show. Then make a graph of your findings.

TV show	1	2	3	4	5	6	7	8	9	10	11	12	13	14	15	16	17	18	19	20	21	22	23	24	25	26	27	28	29	30
Sport																														
News																														
Cartoons																														
Nature																														
Current affairs																														
Soaps																														
Dramas																														

Graph your results below:

30
29
28
27
26
25
24
23
22
21
20
19
18
17
16
15
14
13
12
11
10
9
8
7
6
5
4
3
2
1

Sports News Cartoons Nature Current Affairs Soaps Dramas

66

Brilliant Publications

This page may be reproduced by the original purchaser for non-commercial classroom use.

Timely Tasks for Fast Finishers 7–9 Year Olds

© Blake Publishing

Making decisions

(a) A new girl has joined your class. Today is her first day. She cannot speak English very well and she is very shy. What are some things you could do to make her feel welcome?

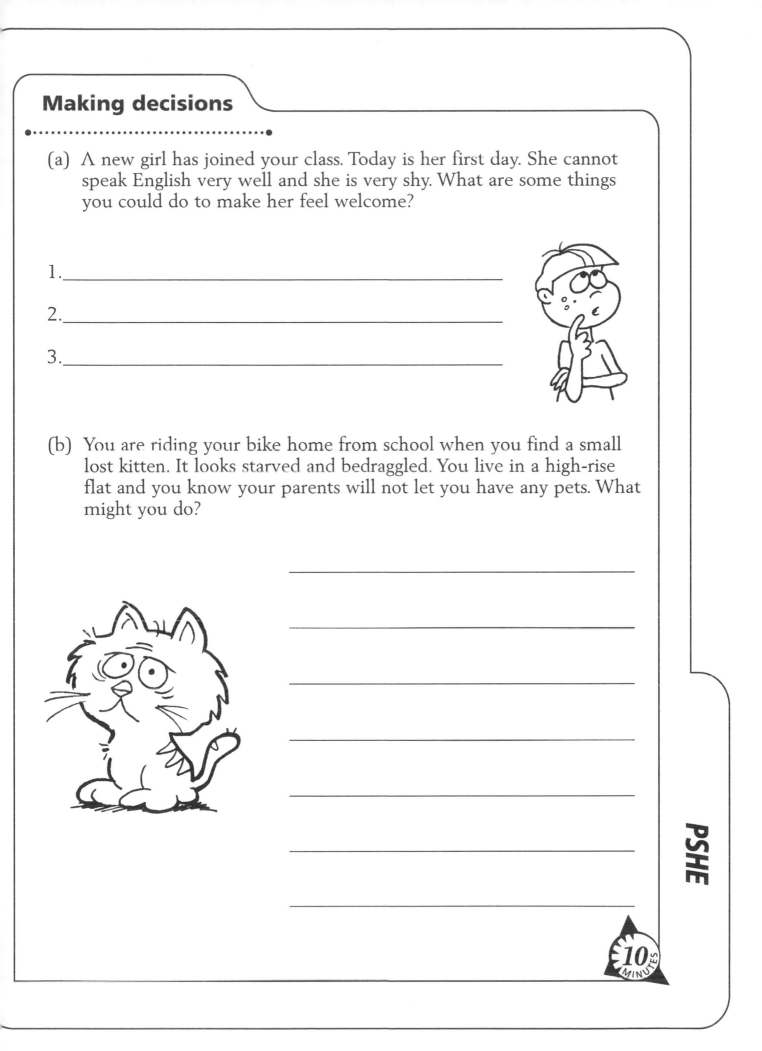

1._____

2._____

3._____

(b) You are riding your bike home from school when you find a small lost kitten. It looks starved and bedraggled. You live in a high-rise flat and you know your parents will not let you have any pets. What might you do?

_____

_____

_____

_____

_____

_____

PSHE

10 MINUTES

Brilliant Publications

This page may be reproduced by the original purchaser for non-commercial classroom use.

Timely Tasks for Fast Finishers 7–9 Year Olds

© Blake Publishing

67

English

Page 4
Connections
1. horse/saddle
2. scales/fish
3. down/duck
4. paper/pen
5. camel/hump
6. bottle/glass
7. silk/worm
8. kidney/heart

Page 5
Same letters
1. ate/tea
2. flow/wolf
3. wasp/paws
4. lump/plum
5. lame/meal
6. tame/meat
7. lair/rail
8. read/dare
9. edit/tide
10. bleat/table
11. care/race
12. star/rats

Cramped words
1. sick
2. lion
3. snake
4. four
5. pony
6. first
7. city
8. dry
9. pink
10. duck
11. shoes
12. mouse

Page 6
Starters
1. Camel
2. Kitten
3. Bee
4. Elephant
5. Milk
6. Twenty
7. Dog
8. Saucer
9. Ladder
10. Ice
leaves ape / pea

Small words
1. platypus
2. hedgehog
3. penguin
4. monkey
5. sparrow
6. swallow
7. rabbit
8. stork
9. parrot
10. pelican

Page 7
Codes
1. horse
2. donkey
3. zebra
4. mouse
5. goat
6. tiger
7. sparrow
8. robin
9. eagle
10. swallow
11. penguin
12. elephant

Picture this
Brigit
bat
branches
bark
bird
bee
balloon
bell
bush
berries
bricks
bottle
bag
box
boy
bike
basket
bread
bucket

Page 8
Codes
1. meat
2. cake
3. butter
4. bread
5. jam
6. salad

Three's a crowd
1. two
2. toy
3. ham
4. cod
5. mat
6. ewe
7. pen
8. all
9. rat
10. gem
11. ant
12. map
13. arm
14. sad
15. run
16. hue
17. ice
18. nod
19. odd
20. sea
21. gun
22. ear
23. eel
24. wed

Page 9
Twin words
1. sauce
2. groom
3. chips
4. ball
5. jam
6. pepper
7. fork
8. downs

Page 10
Back to front
1. balloon
2. sparrow
3. football
4. winter
5. yellow
6. strawberry
7. flour
8. money
9. cheese
10. finger
11. pony
12. doctor
13. jungle
14. chair
15. birthday
16. people
17. elephant
18. stable/tables

Brilliant Publications

© Blake Publishing

Page 11
Magic squares
tank
Alan
name
knee
stir
tide
idea
reap

Classifying
Colours—crimson, purple, violet, yellow

Vegetables—cabbage, lettuce, turnip, marrow

Birds—ostrich, penguin, sparrow, swallow

Reptiles—gecko, crocodile, lizard, snake

Page 12
Odd one out
1. owl—the others aren't birds
2. fox—the others are clothes
3. rib—the others are numbers
4. cup—the others are insects
5. sat—the others are foods

Page 13
Hidden word
1. hamburger
2. peach
3. banana
4. butter
5. cheese
6. margarine
7. lemon
8. apricot

Missing vowels
1. antelope
2. school
3. tennis
4. question
5. tractor
6. octagon
7. newspaper
8. mountain
9. magpie
10. lizard
11. lettuce
12. library

Page 14
'One' builder
cone, bone, done, gone, lone, tone, money, stone, telephone, zone

Make a word
best, bust, cast, cost, dust, east, fast, fist, gist, gust, hist, host, jest, just, last, lest, list, lost, lust, mast, mist, most, must, nest, past, pest, post, rest, rust, test, vast, vest, west, zest

Dictionary dazzle
fruit, insect, bird, cat, horse, fish, pig, strings, money, wheels

Page 15
Word road
To, get, her, together, the, era, rat, rate, at, ate, ten, no, not, note, tea, team, me

Same and different
DIFFICULT hard easy,
BROAD wide narrow,
START begin end,
FALL drop rise,
WET damp dry,
DANGER peril safety,
UNHAPPY sad cheery,
LOFTY tall short,
LISTEN hear talk,
FEEBLE weak strong

Page 16
Adding letters
hand, coat, frog, nest, pine, ship, scar, bait, bread, stairs, barn

Letter rows
1. 5
2. 1 and 2
3. 3
4. 4
5. 6
6. stop, post, pots, tops, spot

Page 17
Unscrambles
soft/duck, gold/hand, long/rich, song/coat, read/draw, foot/moon, wool/stop, west/wing, feet/ball, bell/sock

Missing letters
banana, peach, pear, apricot, nectarine, mandarin, grape, apple, pineapple, plum, orange, lemon

Page 18
Twos
fly/bee, zebra/tiger, chin/nose, table/chair, seven/eight, wheel/motor

Page 19
Small words
ham, rob, jam, bed, bag, eight, fur, aunt, red, pan

To be or not to be
bed, bee, bell, beard, bear, beak, beneath, berry, bean or beetroot, begin

Page 20
Jumble joins
raincoat, moonlight, lifeboat, notebook, crossroad, toothbrush, photograph, hitchhiker, spaceship, honeycomb

Join them up
onion, monkey, gold, cream, sparrow, meat, pink, stable, kitten, ladder

Page 21
Add a letter
zebra, lion, giraffe, camel, donkey, tortoise, elephant, squirrel, gorilla, horse

Which letter?
1. t
2. r
3. u
4. e
5. w
6. m

ANSWERS

Page 22
Find the word
1. cauliflower
2. rainbow
3. write
4. eleven
5. cauliflower
6. write
7. thorough
8. thorough

Page 23
Picture puzzle
i) shake
ii) please
iii) dear
iv) home
v) sleep

Maths

Page 24
Pattern puzzle
1. + 14, 14, 17, 18, 21, 24, 24, 24, 23, 30, 33
2. x 15, 18, 28, 20, 24, 25, 45, 14, 40, 100, 24
3. – 7, 6, 10, 11, 5, 6, 9, 29, 6, 5, 80

Three's a crowd
Numbers not part of 3 x table: seven, ten, eleven, thirteen

Page 25
Circling around
+3 5, 6, 13, 8, 9, 10, 15, 7
x3 9, 12, 18, 15, 30, 24, 21, 27
-3 7, 12, 17, 97, 37, 15, 9, 27
÷3 3, 4, 5, 7, 6, 10, 12, 8

Page 26
Numbers for letters
10
13
4
21
4
17
6
7
1
21
20
20

Number words
1. zebra
2. apple
3. broom
4. green
5. mouse
6. butter

Page 27
All tied up
24 5
12 1
40 3
30 2

Page 28
Missing numbers
6
14
6
48
21
32

What am I?
1. 9
2. 4
3. 17
4. 18
5. 24

Page 29
How far to go?
ant 14.5 cm
ladybird 15 cm
caterpillar 14 cm

Magic squares
9		
4	0	5
4	3	2
1	6	2

9		
1	6	2
4	3	2
4	0	5

9		
1	4	4
6	3	0
2	2	5

12		
5	5	2
1	4	7
6	3	3

12		
3	3	6
7	4	1
2	5	5

15		
8	3	4
1	5	9
6	7	2

Page 30
Quick quiz
1. Tuki
2. Joanne
3. Paul
4. apples
5. apples

Codes
1. clock
2. stove
3. chair
4. kettle
5. fruit
6. cheese
7. table
8. heater

Page 31
Quick calculations
1. 15
2. 10
3. 10
4. 19
5. 16
6. 20
7. 12
8. 15
9. 17
10. 14
11. 10
12. 165
13. 24
14. 9
15. 32
16. 50
17. 11, 13, 15, 17, 19
18. 109

Number puzzle
Across
1. 180
3. 44
5. 2331

Down
1. 1421
2. 843
3. 111

Brilliant Publications

© Blake Publishing

Price lists

peach £1.65
salt £1.55
butter £2.40
milk £1.65
bread £1.65
flour £2.00
meat £1.15
sugar £1.85

Page 32
Following rows
1. 3→6→10→20→
    30→25→25
2. 10→5→15→30→
    50→80→100→100
3. 8→16→36→31→
    62→70→140→140

Class quiz
1. 7
2. 1
3. 5
4. 7
5. 8
6. 4

Page 33
Fruit loops
1. pear
2. apple
3. peach
4. banana
5. orange
6. grape

Flags and poles
3x4=2x6
10x2=5x4
6x5=3x10
6x3=2x9
4x4=2x8
8x5=2x20
8x3=2x12
10x5=2x25

Page 34
Big and small
1. b
2. c
3. b
4. b

Page 35
Circle sums
1. 7+8
2. 9+11
3. 7+5
4. 10+11
5. 16+8
6. 9+7
7. 11+7
8. 10+20

Page 36
Sum of it
yellow 18, red 12,
pink 26, brown 35, green 33,
dark blue 13, black 24, light
blue 25

Find the total
1. 7
2. 32
3. 5
4. 48

Page 37
Zapping
3+4+8+10
3+6+7+9
4+6+7+8

Page 38
Squares
55 squares

Rectangles
25 rectangles

Page 39
Cubes
30 cubes

Triangles
10 triangles

Twenties

Green	Yellow	Green	Yellow
Yellow	Green	Yellow	Yellow
Green	Green	Yellow	Green
Yellow	Green	Green	Green
Green	Yellow	Yellow	Yellow

Page 40
Missing numbers
2, 2, 4, 3, 3, 2, 4, 8, 2, 6, 4, 4

Number knowledge
692, 39, 692, 291, 563,
365/563
692 – 563 – 481 – 365 – 291
– 123 – 39

Page 41
Adding squares
a) 9
b) 15
c) 24
d) 30
e) 27, f) 60

Costings
1. 40p
2. 65p
3. £1.20
4. £1.00
5. £1.20
6. £1.25

Page 42
Relations
1. 8   4. 10
2. 9   5. 16
3. 6   6. 3

Fishy tales
Alex (odd) 3 x 5,
7 x 5, 5 x 5, 3 x 7,
3 x 3, 7 x 3, 5 x 3,
12 + 7, 15 + 6, 12 + 9
Nina (even) 3 x 4,
8 + 8, 4 x 4, 7 x 2,
9 x 2, 6 x 2, 5 x 4,
12 x 2, 7 + 5

Page 43
Letters and numbers
1. 6
2. 29
3. 19
4. 1
5. 3
6. baby, paid, dead, toad

Correct boxes

Thinking
Page 47
Shaping up
A3

B5

C2

D1

E4

ANSWERS

Page 51
Look and think
B

Page 52
Squaring up

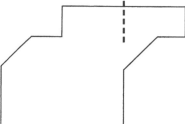

Shape words
A stitch in time saves nine.

A bird in the hand is worth two in the bush.

Page 53
It will amaze you

Eye tricks
C

Page 55
Shadows
squirrel
cockatoo
monkey
rhinoceros
snake
kangaroo
orangutan
shark
camel
owl

Page 56
Spot the error
The shadows are in the wrong direction.

The bicycle has only half a chain.

Science

Page 60
Energy
Electricity mains–power to homes, offices, factories, hospitals, etc.

Electric battery–toys, torches, remote controls, radios, etc.

Wind–windmills, yachts.

Petrol–cars, trucks, buses, etc.

Sunlight–plants, solar batteries.

Food–people, pets, other animals.

Page 61
Living things
Mammals–badger, pig, lion.

Reptiles–crocodile, lizard, alligator.

Birds–penguin, sparrow, eagle.

Insects–beetle, wasp, ladybird.

The fish is a haddock.

Page 62
Our environment
Grey squirrel – it has been crowding out the native red squirrel; it damages trees because of its nesting habits.

Mink – it is blamed for the extinction of the water vole; it kills and eats waterfowl.

Explain the error

1. It's necessary to plug the lead into the electricity supply in order to make the television work.

2. With the sun directly behind the tree, the shadow should fall in front of it.

3. The elephant has a horse's tail.

4. It can never rain on the Moon as the Moon has no air or water.

Humanities

Page 63
Wordsearch
legend	sword
knight	horse
armour	dragon
battle	treasure
damsel	castle
courage	spear

Page 64
People in the community
1. A baker makes bread, cakes and pies.
2. A police officer maintains the law.
3. A teacher helps people learn skills.
4. A carpenter builds and erects houses.
5. A veterinary surgeon cares for sick or injured animals.
6. A chemist dispenses medicines.
7. A hairdresser cuts and cares for people's hair.
8. A mechanic repairs cars.

Page 65
Rules
Football – the governing body; the referee.

Traffic rules – the government; the traffic division of the police force.

Child's game – tradition and children themselves; children playing the game.

Watching TV – parent or guardian; parent or guardian.

In the past
Axe–chainsaw.
Record player–CD or MP3 player.
Scythe–lawn mower/combine harvester.
Hand sewing–sewing machine.

Brilliant Publications